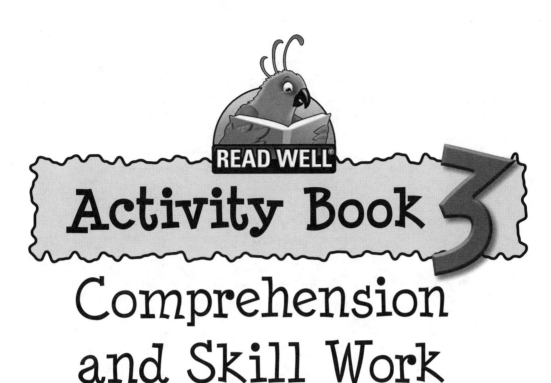

Activity Book 3

Comprehension and Skill Work

Units 13-20

Cambium
LEARNING® Group | Voyager LEARNING

ISBN-13: 978-1-60218-566-1
ISBN-10: 1-60218-566-2
167169/06-14

Printed in the United States of America

Published and Distributed by

17855 Dallas Parkway, Suite 400 • Dallas, TX 75287 • 800 547-6747
www.voyagerlearning.com

CREDITS

1: ©istockphoto.com/Eric Isselée. 3: Funnel web ©Punchstock, cobweb ©istockphoto.com/Jakob Dam Knudsen, orb web ©Gary W. Carter/Corbis. 4: Spider ©istockphoto.com/Thomas Bedenk, fly ©Kai's Power Photos. 5, 13, 14–16: Illustrated by Karen Perrins. 6, 8, 30, 53, 55, 60: Illustrated by Steve Clark. 7: ©istockphoto.com/Nico Smit. 9: ©istockphoto.com/geotrack. 10, 19: Spider anatomy ©Photodisc. 11: ©istockphoto.com/Pauline Mills. 19–21: Animals ©Clipart.com, human ©istockphoto.com/Milorad Zaric. 22: Bat skeleton ©Jupiter Images, 22, 25: Illustration by Anton Petrov. 23–24: Bats ©Merlin D. Tuttle, Bat Conservation International. 24: Insect ©Artville. 29: Native Americans by tipi ©Montana Historical Society/L.A. Huffman, pioneers with covered wagons ©Denver Public Library/Western History Collection, covered wagon train ©Clipart.com, children in school ©Kansas State Historical Society. 30: Buffalo ©istockphoto.com/Michael Thompson. 31, 34, 40: Illustrated by Wilson Ong. 31: Betsy's diary ©istockphoto.com/Janne Ahvo. 37: Sod house ©istockphoto.com/Shaun Lowe. 39: ©istockphoto.com/Kriss Russell. 42–47: Pecos Bill and Slue-Foot Sue illustrated by Valeria Docampo. 49, 62: Sun ©Jupiter Images. 49: Grass ©istockphoto.com/fotosav, rabbit ©istockphoto.com/Graeme Purdy, wolf ©istockphoto.com/Neal McClimon. 50: ©Jupiter Images. 51: ©Jupiter Images. 52: Leaf ©istockphoto.com/fajean, giraffe ©istockphoto.com/Kitch Bain, lion ©istockphoto.com/Kristian Sekulic. 56: Whale ©istockphoto.com/David Pruter, cow ©istockphoto.com/Laurent Renault. 58: ©istockphoto.com/Antonio Nunes. 59: Illustrated by Tatjana Mai-Wyss. 61: Clown fish ©istockphoto.com/Jason Lai, giant clam ©Punchstock, coral ©Punchstock. 62, 68–71: Illustrated by Ruth Galloway. 63–66, 80: Illustrated by Page Eastburn-O'Rourke. 67: Octopus ©istockphoto.comherve Lavigne, coral polyp ©istockphoto.com/Adrian Baddeley, nudibranch ©istockphoto.com/Loh Siew Seong, bottom slug ©istockphoto.com/Christopher Waters. 68: ©istockphoto.com/Ian Scott. 72: Jessica and Marilyn Sprick ©Sprick. 74–79, 81–98: Illustrated by Eldon Doty.

Table of Contents

Teachers: If you are using the Activity Book, tear out and staple pages 1–4 to make a Research Notes folder.

Name _____

Locating Information
An Eight-Legged Creature

In this unit, you will take research notes and write your own report. Very cool! You will take notes on topics that you think are interesting. The first one has been done for you. Look in your storybook on page 10. The first topic is Spider Parts. Can you find the facts in this section of your storybook?

Topic: <u>Spider Parts</u> ◁ heading _____

    Fact 1: <u>eight legs</u> _____

    Fact 2: <u>two body parts</u> _____

    Fact 3: <u>not insects, arachnids</u> _____

There are three more topics in this chapter. Select two topics that you think are interesting, and write three facts about each topic. Write down facts that you think are interesting.

Topic: _____

    Fact 1: _____

    Fact 2: _____

    Fact 3: _____

Topic: _____

    Fact 1: _____

    Fact 2: _____

    Fact 3: _____

Save your notes for your report!

Note Taking 2

Name _____

Locating Information
Icky, Sticky Webs

There are two topics in Chapter 2. Write the topics. Then write three facts about each topic. Look in your storybook on page 16. (You can use the heading or your own words for the topics.)

Topic: _____

　　　Fact 1: _____

　　　_____

　　　Fact 2: _____

　　　_____

　　　Fact 3: _____

　　　_____

Topic: _____

　　　Fact 1: _____

　　　_____

　　　Fact 2: _____

　　　_____

　　　Fact 3: _____

　　　_____

Spiders are not insects.
Spiders are classified as

_____

Unit 13 Research Notes

Note Taking 3

Name _____

Compare and Contrast
Webs, So Strong

1 **Complete the following Matrix Chart.** If you need to, look in your storybook.

Type of Web	Shape	Main Use
Funnel Web	• like a funnel • big at the top • small at the _____	to trap food
Cobweb	• no _____ • mess of _____ • tangled	to trap _____
Orb Web	• round and _____ • a spiral around spokes from center	_____ _____

2 **Write three facts about spiders without webs.** Look in your storybook on page 24.

Topic: _____

Fact 1: _____

_____

Fact 2: _____

_____

Fact 3: _____

_____

Note Taking 4

Name _____

Locating Information

A Spider's Life

The three topics in Chapter 4 are: Carnivores, Protection, and Helpful Spiders. Select two topics. Then write three facts about each topic.

Topic: _____

    Fact 1: _____

    _____

    Fact 2: _____

    _____

    Fact 3: _____

    _____

Topic: _____

    Fact 1: _____

    _____

    Fact 2: _____

    _____

    Fact 3: _____

    _____

Unit 13 Activity 1
Use after Exercise 1 and Chapter 1

Name _____

Passage Reading Fluency

1. Practice these words:

Ming	spiderling	emerged	egg sac

2. Read the story 2 times. Cross out a spider each time you read the story.

Ming, the Spiderling

Ming, the Spiderling, emerged from her egg sac along with her   11
brother and sister spiderlings. Ming wasn't sure she was happy to be   23
a spider.   25

"I wish I were an insect," said Ming to her brother and sister. "I   39
wanted wings!"   41

"Be happy you are a spider, Ming," said her brother. "You have   53
eight legs. Insects have only six legs. You may not have wings like   66
some insects, but you have special grip pads on your feet. You can't fly, 80
but you can walk up walls! We spiders are awesome!"   90

"You can also hear very well, even though you don't have ears,"   102
said Ming's sister. "The hairs on your body pick up sound vibrations.   114
This will help you get food."   120

"Maybe being a spider is not bad after all," thought Ming.   131

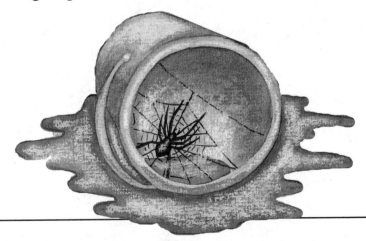

3. Set a timer and see how far you can read in one minute.
   Then cross out the timer.

Unit 13 Activity 2
Use after Exercise 2 and Chapter 2

Name _____

Passage Reading Fluency

1. Practice these words:

spinnerets	threads	scurry	fangs

2. Read the story 2 times. Cross out a spiderweb each time you read the story.

Ming, the Spider, Learns to Use Her Silk

Ming grew up quickly. Soon she was a fine adult spider. She   12
decided that it was fun to be a spider after all. She learned to make   27
silk using her spinnerets. The silk threads she made were stronger than 39
steel threads. She used her silk threads to build a beautiful web.   51

Ming never went hungry. She used her web to trap insects. When   63
an insect flew into her web, she would scurry over and bite the insect 77
with her fangs. She would eat the insect right away or wrap it in silk. 92
By wrapping the insect in silk, Ming could save and eat the insect later. 106

Sometimes, Ming traveled away from her spiderweb. When she   115
did this, she used her silk to make a dragline. When she needed to go   130
home, she just followed the dragline back to her web. Ming always   142
knew how to get home. Ming thought, "I am glad I am a spider."   156

3. Set a timer and see how far you can read in one minute.
   Then cross out the timer.

Unit 13 Activity 3
Use after Exercise 3 and Chapter 3

Name _____

Passage Reading Fluency

1. Practice these words:

patiently	carnivore	clever	vibrations

2. Read the story 2 times. Cross out a spider each time you read the story.

Fishing Spiders

Floating on a leaf in the pond, a fishing spider patiently waits for   13
its next meal. Like all spiders, the fishing spider is a carnivore. It likes   27
to eat meat. Unlike most spiders, the fishing spider does not spin a web   41
to trap its meal. Instead, this spider has a clever way to catch its food.   56

The fishing spider spends most of its day floating in the water on a   70
leaf. It keeps its front legs touching the water. When the fishing spider   83
feels vibrations, it knows that there is an insect or a tiny fish nearby.   97

If an insect is on the surface of the water, or a tiny fish is swimming   113
close by, the fishing spider quickly grabs it and has a fine meal.   126

3. Set a timer and see how far you can read in one minute.
   Then cross out the timer.

Unit 13 Activity 4
Use after Exercise 4 and Chapter 4

Name _____

Main Idea and Supporting Details

> Spiders can be found in many different places all over the world. Some spiders live in gardens. Others live in deserts. Still others live in the mountains. Many live in your homes. Spiders can live in many places, but they usually live alone.

1 **What is this paragraph about?** _____

2 **Supporting Details: Spiders live in . . .**
List the details.

- _____

- _____

- _____

- _____

Main Idea:

Spiders live . . .

_____

_____

○ in deserts.
○ all over the world.
○ in gardens.

3 **Write the main idea.** Be sure to start your sentence with a capital letter.

_____

_____

8

Unit 13 Report Writing

Teachers: If you are using the Activity Book, tear out and staple pages 9–12 to make a report folder.

Title Page: Write the title of your report and your name on the lines below.

_____

by _____

Date_____

◆ **INTRODUCTION** • 1. Introduce the subject. Include at least one fascinating fact to interest the reader.
2. Next, select and introduce two topics.

Spiders are _____ creatures. _____

_____

_____

_____

This report is about _____

_____

_____

_____

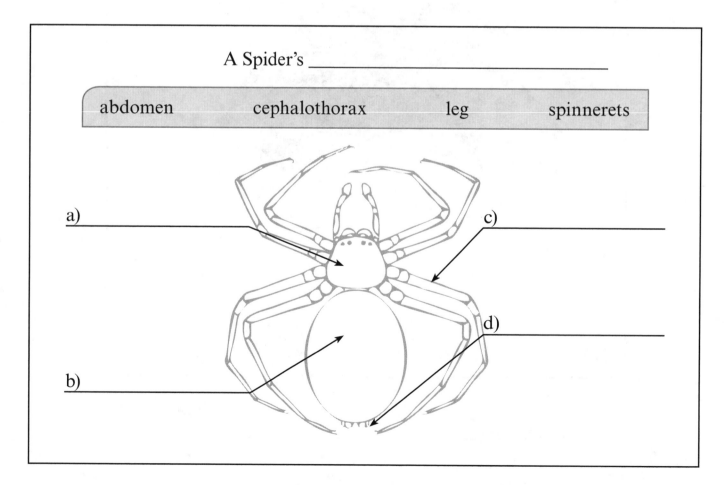

A Spider's _____

| abdomen | cephalothorax | leg | spinnerets |

a) _____

c) _____

b) _____

d) _____

1ST TOPIC • Select a topic. Complete the topic sentence. Then write at least two facts about the topic.

One of the most interesting things about spiders is _____

_____

_____

_____

_____

_____

2ND TOPIC • Select a second topic. Complete the topic sentence. Then write at least three facts about the topic.

Another interesting thing about spiders is _____

_____

_____

_____

_____

Spider, Spider, on the Wall

▲ **ENDING** • Write a paragraph that tells your reader how you feel about spiders. You may want to end your report with what else you'd like to learn. Then draw a picture in the box.

Now that I know more about spiders, I _____

_____

_____

_____

_____

_____

_____

_____

Unit 13 Activity 5
Use after Exercise 7, Introduction, and Chapter 1

Name _____

Story Comprehension
Introduction and Chapter 1, A Mountain Full of Animals

1 **A legend is a story that . . .**
   ○ is about animals.
   ○ is told from generation to generation.

2 **Who is telling the legend?**
   ○ Gray Cloud is telling the legend.
   ○ Gray Cloud's grandfather is telling the legend.

3 **When does the legend take place?**
   ○ yesterday, back in the woods
   ○ long, long ago, back in space
   ○ long, long ago, back in the very beginning

4 **Check five creatures that lived in the mountain caves.**
   __ the Winged Ones   __ reptiles and amphibians
   __ mammals, the Four-Footed Ones   __ insects
   __ spacemen, the High Flyers   __ the water creatures

5 **Why were the animals excited?** If you need to, look in your storybook on page 48.

   The animals were excited because _____

   _____

   _____

6 **Who do you think Gray Cloud may retell the legend to someday?**

   Gray Cloud _____

   _____

   _____

Name _____

Maze Reading and Paragraph Comprehension

When you come to the words between the parentheses, circle the word that makes the most sense in the paragraph.

Centipedes

Did you know that the word *centipede* means 100-footed?

Do centipedes really have 100 feet? (Some, Purple, She) centipedes have 100 feet, and others (swim, have, boy) as few as 30. Even 30 (feet, and, head) is a lot of feet!

Centipedes (make, tall, can) be between one and 12 inches (smile, long, blue). They live all over the world. (They, He, But) like habitats that are damp and (protected, boring, you). You can find them under stones, (computers, the, leaves), or rotten bark. Centipedes can live (on, run, for) a long time. In fact, some (giraffes, hike, centipedes) have been known to live up (by, to, plain) six years.

1 **Reread the passage. Does it make sense?**   yes   No, but I fixed it.

2 **What does the word *centipede* mean?**
   ○ 100 feet   ○ 100 heads   ○ 30 feet

Try to use a snazzy word: **habitat creature**

3 **Describe where you can find centipedes.**
Write at least two sentences. Use facts from the paragraph.

_____

_____

_____

_____

Unit 14 Activity 1
Use after Exercise 1, Introduction, and Chapters 1, 2

Name _____

Story Comprehension
Introduction and The Birds and the Mammals Get Angry

1 **In the Introduction, Gray Cloud asked, "Why . . .**

_____

2 **When did the legend take place?**

○ long ago   ○ in the forest   ○ when the world was new

3 **The legend began with a problem. What was the problem?**
(Start with *The birds and the mammals . . .*)

_____

_____

4 **Where was Bat during the war between the birds and the mammals?**

○ with the birds   ○ with the mammals   ○ hiding inside a hollow tree

5 **How did Bat trick the mammals?**
(Start with *Bat tricked the mammals by . . .*)

_____

_____

_____

○ hiding his wings and showing his sharp teeth
○ hiding his sharp teeth and showing his tail

6 **Bat is the trickster in this legend. What do you think will happen to him at the end of the story?**

○ Bat will live happily ever after.
○ Bat will only be able to come out at night.

Name _____

Vocabulary and Alphabetical Order

1. Fill in the missing letters of the alphabet.

★ 2. Find words in your storybook that begin with different letters, and put them in alphabetical order. Two are done for you. Find at least three more.

3. For each word, complete the definition. Then write a sentence using the word.

4. Draw a picture in the box.

arachnid

C centipede

F

I

L

O

Q

R

T

U

W

XYZ

creature • A creature is _____

_____

Write a sentence using the word *creature*.

_____

_____

_____

_____

legend • A legend is a _____ that is told from one generation to the next.

Write a sentence using the word *legend*.

_____

_____

_____

trickster • A trickster is a character who tries to

_____

Write a sentence using the word *trickster*.

_____

_____

_____

_____

16

Name _____

Visualizing and Illustrating
The War Between Birds and Mammals

Read and complete the sentences to retell the story. Illustrate each part of the story.

1 **Long, long ago, the birds and the mammals began a war because they did not want to share the**

_____

2 **When the mammals won, they had**

a _____

Bat showed the Four-Footed Ones

that he was a _____

3 **When the birds won, they had a**

_____

Bat showed the Winged Ones that

he was a _____

4 **The mammals and birds made a new rule for Bat. They said he had**

to _____

_____

_____

Unit 14 Activity 4
Use after Exercise 2 and Chapter 3

Name _____

Story Comparison

Complete the matrix below to compare the two legends you read. Circle whether the story element is the same or different.

Legend	Centipede and Grandmother Spider	The War Between Birds and Mammals	Same or Different
Setting Where and When	• in the mountains • when the world was new	• _____ • long, long ago	same different
Main Trickster	_____	_____	same different
Problem	Centipede didn't have enough legs.	The birds and the mammals _____ _____ _____	same different
Action	While the insects slept, Centipede stole two legs from each insect and put them on himself.	While the animals were at war, Bat hid. When the mammals won, he pretended he was a mammal. When the birds won, he pretended he was a bird.	same different
Conclusion for the Trickster	Centipede was told _____ _____	Bat was told _____ _____ _____	(same) (Both were punished.)
Lesson for the Trickster	Don't try to _____ _____	Don't try to _____ _____	same different

18

What's What?

by _____

Animal Classification Chart

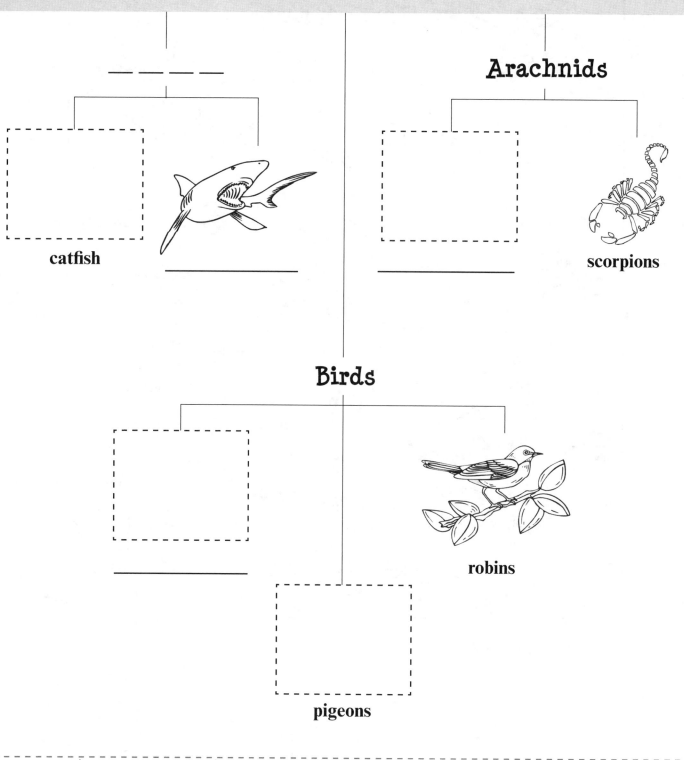

Arachnids

catfish

scorpions

Birds

robins

pigeons

When you classify things, you put them into groups according to their characteristics. Match the cut-out pictures to the appropriate boxes to create a classification chart. Then fill in the blank lines with the names of the animals or groups.

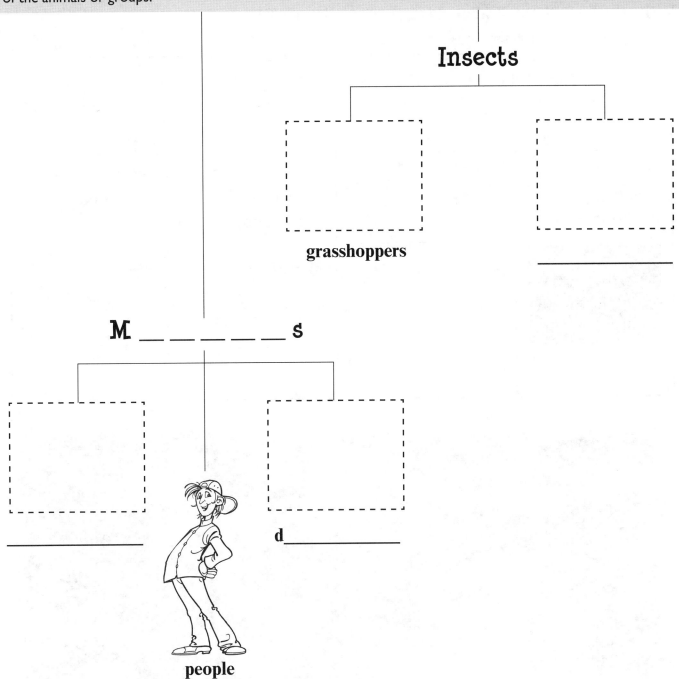

Insects

grasshoppers

_____

M _ _ _ _ _ s

_____

d_____

people

Congratulations! You are a classification whiz!

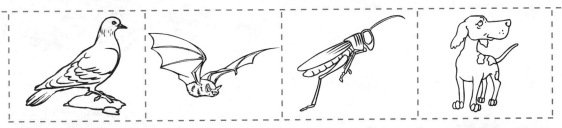

Bird or Mammal?

Write the facts that tell what class, or group, bats are in.

If you need to, look in your storybook.

Topic/Main Idea: Bats are _____

Fact 1 (page 82)

They have backbones.

Fact 2 (page 82)

They have

_____

_____

Fact 3 (page 82)

They do not lay eggs. They

_____

_____

_____

_____

Fact 4 (page 82)

They take care of

_____

_____

Unit 14 Activity 5
Use after Exercise 4 and Chapters 2 and 3

Name _____

Main Idea and Supporting Details

> A bat's wings make it an incredible flying machine. The wings are connected to arm bones that flap like a bird. The wings are also made of a thin skin that billows like a sail. Finally, the bat moves its wings with long thin fingers that allow it to turn quickly. A bat's wings are amazing.

1 What is this paragraph about? _____

2 Supporting Details
List the details.

- arm bones that flap like a bird

- _____
  _____
  _____

- _____
  _____

★ **3** Write the main idea.
(Start with *A bat's wings . . .*)

_____
_____
_____
_____
_____

Unit 14 Activity 6

Name _____

Passage Comprehension
Flying Machine

1 **Locate means to** _____

2 **What is echolocation?** If you need to, reread the "Bat Senses" section in Chapter 2.

    O locating something by using balls that bounce back to you

    O locating something by using sounds that bounce back to you

3 **Look at the diagram below. It shows how bats use echolocation to locate their prey.**

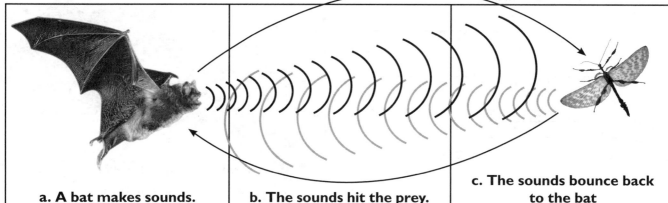

| a. A bat makes sounds. | b. The sounds hit the prey. | c. The sounds bounce back to the bat |

4 **Describe how a bat uses echolocation to locate food.**

First, _____

Next, _____

_____

_____

Then, _____

_____

_____

Bats know where their prey is based
on the sounds that bounce back to them!

Name _____

Passage Reading Fluency

1. Practice these words:

although	Jennifer	Uncle Randy	swoop	mosquitoes

2. Read the story 2 times. Cross out a bat each time you read the story.

Waiting for the Little Brown Bats

It was almost dark. Jennifer asked her Uncle Randy, "Do you think we will see a bat tonight?"   11 / 18

Uncle Randy said, "I am sure we will. We have bats that live under the deck during the day. Every evening they come out looking for food."   31 / 43 / 45

Jennifer was excited. She had never seen a bat before. She was visiting her relatives for the summer. These visits were always special. Jennifer got to walk in the woods, feed squirrels, and look for bats. "What kind of bats will we see? What do they eat?" asked Jennifer.   57 / 68 / 81 / 94

Uncle Randy answered, "We have little brown bats. These bats are common around here. They eat moths, wasps, beetles, and mosquitoes. Did you know that they eat about 1,200 mosquitoes in an hour? We like bats!"   104 / 114 / 126 / 130

Just then, Jennifer saw a dark shadow swoop out from under the deck. She smiled. It was feeding time for the little brown bats.   142 / 154

3. Set a timer and see how far you can read in one minute.
   Then cross out the timer.

Name _____

Fact Summary • Locating Information
Little Brown Bats

1 **In this chapter, you learned about the most common bat in North America. Write facts that tell why these ordinary little animals are very interesting.**
If you need to, look in your storybook.

> **Topic/Main idea:** Little brown bats are incredible.

Fact 1 (page 97)	**Fact 2** (page 98)	**Fact 3** (page 98)	**Fact 4** (page 99)
• can eat	• _____	• _____	• _____

2 **Use the facts to write a fact summary about little brown bats.** (Start with *Little brown bats are incredible . . .*)

(Topic Sentence) _____

(Fact) _____

(Fact) _____

(Conclusion) _____

Unit 15 Activity 1
Use after Exercise 1, Introduction, and Chapters 1, 2

Name _____

Story Comprehension
Buffalo Hunt

1 **Setting: When and where does the story take place?**

When: _____

Where: _____

2 **Initiating Event: Why was this a special day for Many Falls and Dark Cloud?**
- ○ The boys were eleven and going to have a birthday party.
- ○ The boys were eleven and going on their first buffalo hunt.
- ○ The boys were going to learn to ride a horse.

3 **Action: What happened on the buffalo hunt?**
You may wish to look in your storybook.

1. The scouts led the men to a herd of _____

2. The hunters yelled and rode fast. The herd started _____

3. The lead hunter drove one _____ away from the rest.

4. Many Falls and the other hunters fired their _____

4 **Cause and Effect: How a main character got his name.**

Action		Outcome
• fell many times		• named _____

Action		Outcome
• quickly shot an arrow		• named _____

Unit 15 Activity 2
Use after Exercise 1, Introduction, and Chapters 1, 2

Name _____

Passage Comprehension • Main Idea
The Mighty Buffalo

1 **Fill in the chart below to tell how American Indians used the buffalo.**

Buffalo part: What it was used for:

Page 15 • small bones	• knives
Page 15 • stomach	• _____
Page 15 • gallstones	• _____
Page 15 • brains	• _____
Page 16 • _____	• _____
Page 16 • _____	• _____
Page 16 • _____	• _____

2 **Main Idea:** When American Indians killed a buffalo, they _____

_____

American West Timeline

1800–1900

by _____

In each box, draw a picture to illustrate the year and story. Then write about the important event that took place during that time period in the space below the picture. You will complete a little of the timeline each day.

1835	1843	1850

Buffalo Hunt

A River Crossing

_____

_____

_____

_____

_____

_____

_____

Life on the Trail

Pioneers journeyed west in

covered wagons. The trip

took six months!

_____

| 1863 | 1869 | 1885 | 1886 |

The Great Railroad

[ ]

_____

_____

_____

_____

Betsy's New Home

[ ]

_____

_____

_____

_____

Ming Mei, Railroad Worker

_____

_____

_____

_____

Betsy's Diary

January 5, 1886
The weather has been nice. Papa took the wagon to town this morning. He'll stay there until tomorrow. He says he has a surprise for us.

January 6, 1886
Willie and I saw big dark clouds this afternoon. We ran back to the dugout.

_____

_____

_____

Congratulations!

Write your name on the blank line and draw a picture of yourself in the box.

_____ is a historian!

Unit 15 Activity 3
Use after Exercise 2 and Chapter 3

Name _____

Passage Comprehension • Main Idea
Talking Without Words

1 **Communicate means to . . .**

○ talk to yourself.　　○ share ideas or feelings with someone else.

2 **In this chapter, you learned some of the ways American Indian tribes communicated years ago.** Complete the chart. If you need to, look in your storybook.

Topic: American Indians communicated in many ways.

Fact 1 (page 19)	Fact 2 (page 20)	Fact 3 (page 20)
• used _____ _____ to communicate with other tribes that spoke a different language	• used _____ as a way of saying "Our people were here"	• used _____ _____ to communicate over long distances

3 **List three ways you, your friends, and your family communicate with others.**
(One is done for you.)

• e-mail _____

• _____

• _____

4 **List two reasons it is important for you to communicate.**

• to keep in touch with _____

• _____

Name _____

Passage Reading

1. Practice these words:

journey	belongings	sugar	women	breakfast

2. Read the story 2 times. Cross out a covered wagon each time you read the story.

The Journey West

On the first day of our journey west, everyone was excited. We crammed the covered wagons with our belongings. We packed food that would not spoil. We took beans, dried meat, flour, and sugar. We even brought a cow so we would have fresh milk for our six-month journey. Pa says there is good land to farm out west. He says that we can have our own land and build a nice new home.

We have been on the trail for three months now. Three months is a long time. We get up every morning before the sun is up. Everyone has a job to do. My job is to help Pa pull down the tents. Pa says I am a good helper even if I am only seven years old. Ma and the other women make breakfast. My sister helps milk the cow.

We are on the trail every day from when the sun comes up to when the sun goes down. Pa says we can't dawdle, or we will get caught in winter storms. The bumpy wagon ride makes me sick. I would rather walk next to the wagon, but I get tired. Pa says it will take three more months to get to our new home. We can't wait to get there.

Unit 15 Activity 5
Use after Exercise 3 and Chapters 4 and 5

Name _____

Locating Information • Letter Writing

1 The passage from Activity 4, "The Journey West," is historical fiction. That means that even though the story is not true, it is based on facts. List three things about making the journey west in the 1800s. (The first one is done for you.)

• covered wagons packed with belongings

• _____

_____

• _____

_____

2 Write your own historical fiction passage. Pretend you are on a covered wagon traveling west. Use one of the things you listed above to write a letter to your friend in the East.

Dear _____ ,

    We have been on the trail for six months. You would not believe

what it's like. _____

_____

_____

_____

               Your friend,

               _____

Name _____

Maze Reading and Story Comprehension

When you come to the words between the parentheses, circle the word that makes the most sense in the paragraph. Then reread the paragraph to see if it makes sense.

Chinese and Irish immigrants, former slaves, and soldiers built the Great Railroad. They made the ground flat and (dragged, dug, dark) tunnels through the mountains. They laid (inches, steel, hundreds) of miles of track. The work (was, is, there) exhausting and dangerous. The Great Railroad (changed, laughed, though) life in America forever.

Vocabulary and Synonyms

Synonyms are words that mean the same or almost the same.

The railroad workers were *tired* from digging tunnels all day.

When they returned to camp, they were *hungry* and couldn't wait for a good meal.

1 **A synonym for *tired* is** _____

○ rested   ○ exhausted   ○ frantic

2 **The railroad workers were** _____ **from digging tunnels all day.**

○ rested   ○ exhausted   ○ frantic

3 **A synonym for *hungry* is** _____

○ curious   ○ exhausted   ○ ravenous

4 **The railroad workers were** _____ **and couldn't wait for a good meal.**

○ curious   ○ exhausted   ○ ravenous

Unit 15 Activity 7
Use after Exercise 5 and Chapters 8 and 9

Name _____

Passage Comprehension

Sod Houses

When the pioneers headed west, many people built new homes on the prairie. A prairie is like a sea of grass. There are very few trees. With no trees, most pioneers had no wood to build their new homes. The pioneers used what was there. Many people built their first homes of grass and dirt. The houses were called sod houses.

Sod houses were usually just one room. They were dark and damp. When it rained, the sod houses leaked, and the dirt floors turned into mud. The pioneers shared their homes with mice, snakes, and all kinds of insects.

1 This passage is about _____

2 Describe a prairie. A prairie is _____

_____

3 What is sod? Sod is _____

4 I _____ want to live in a sod house because
　　　　　would　　　　　　would not

_____

_____

_____

Unit 15
Use anytime after Chapter 4

Name _____

Just for Fun • Packing the Covered Wagon
What Would You Take?

Pretend you live in America in the 1800s. Your family is moving west. You will be far from friends and family. You have to leave most of your belongings behind. Your clothes have been packed. But you can take one more thing that is very important to you—something that is valuable. What would it be?

1 **Draw a picture of what you would take.**

2 **Tell what you would take and why.**

My family is moving west in a covered wagon. I can take only one thing

besides my clothes. I am taking _____

because _____

_____

_____

Unit 16 Activity 1
Use after Exercise 1 and Chapters 1 and 2

Name _____

Passage Comprehension • Fact Summary
The Cowboy Trail

1 **What was the West like in 1860?**

○ Buffalo and cattle lived in trees.

○ Buffalo and cattle ran free.

○ Buffalo and cattle lived inside fences.

2 **What did we learn about the lives of cowboys in the 1860s?**
If you need to, look in your storybook.

> **Topic/Main Idea:** Cowboys needed strength and courage to work on cattle drives.

Fact 1
• worked from before

_____

to long after

_____

Fact 2
• hot and

_____

Fact 3
List three dangers

• _____

• _____

• _____

3 **Complete the paragraph to explain why cowboys needed strength and courage to work on cattle drives. Write at least two supporting details.**

Cowboys needed strength and _____

_____

_____

_____

Name _____

Story Comprehension
A Cowboy's Story

1 **Tell about the cowboy.** Write at least four words or phrases that describe the narrator.

_____

_____

_____

_____

2 **Before becoming a cowboy, the cowboy worked with his family . . .**

○ in school.   ○ on a farm.   ○ in a truck

3 **What was the cowboy's job?** (Start with what the question is about.)

_____

_____

_____

4 **The story told how cowboys treated each other with respect.**

How did cowboys treat each other with respect? They . . .

__ ate together.   __ would not eat with each other.

__ roped cattle together.   __ would not rope cattle together.

__ sang together.   __ would not sing together.

Main Idea: Cowboys showed each other respect by living and working together.

The Tall Tale of Pecos Bill

Use after Exercise 2, Introduction, and Chapter 1

Name _____

Visualizing and Illustrating
Pecos Bill Becomes a Cowboy

Read and complete the sentences to retell the story. Illustrate each part of the story.

1 **Pecos Bill bounced out of his**

family's _____

_____

2 **Pecos Bill was found and raised**

by a _____

_____

3 **One day, a** _____
told Bill that he was not a coyote
because he did not have a

_____

4 **Pecos Bill decided to become a**
cowboy and raced a horse named

_____

They became _____

The Tall Tale of Pecos Bill

Unit 16 Activity 4
Use after Exercise 2, Introduction, and Chapter 1

Name _____

Genre and Vocabulary
Tall Tales and Exaggeration

Tall tales are imaginative stories. People who tell tall tales exaggerate and make up impossible events. Which of these sentences tell you the stories about Pecos Bill are tall tales?

1 **Pecos Bill wore a cowboy hat.**

    Does this make the story of Pecos Bill a tall tale?   yes   no

2 **Pecos Bill was raised by a coyote mother.**

    Does this make the story of Pecos Bill a tall tale?   yes   no

3 **Widow Maker was a horse.**

    Does this make the story of Pecos Bill a tall tale?   yes   no

4 **Widow Maker ate gunpowder for breakfast.**

    Does this make the story of Pecos Bill a tall tale?   yes   no

5 **Pecos Bill and Widow Maker ran to the North Pole.**

    Does this make the story of Pecos Bill a tall tale?   yes   no

Check and Correct: "Yes" should be circled three times.

©2009 Sopris West Educational Services. All Rights Reserved.

Unit 16 Activity 5
Use after Exercise 3 and Chapter 2

Name _____

Story Comprehension

Pecos Bill Rides a Wild Cyclone

1 At the beginning of the story, who did Pecos Bill see in the Rio Grande?

○ Antonia Ant   ○ Slue-Foot Sue   ○ his coyote mother

2 Check the things that made Slue-Foot Sue bigger than life—a superhuman cowgirl. Slue-Foot Sue . . .

__ rode a 50-foot catfish.   __ loved to dance.

__ wore a cowgirl hat.   __ swung a gator by its tail.

3 In the middle of the story, what was the problem?

○ The sky grew dark, and it started to rain.

○ The sky grew dark, and a cyclone headed for town.

○ The sky grew light, and the sun came out.

4 What do some folks say happened to Bill? (Write a complete sentence.)

_____

_____

_____

5 Check the impossible events and exaggerations that make this a tall tale.

__ Pecos Bill rode the cyclone
for 27 hours a day, 17 days a week.

__ Pecos Bill carved out the
Grand Canyon with his boot heels.

__ Pecos Bill was a cowboy from Texas.

__ Slue-Foot Sue rode a
giant 50-foot catfish.

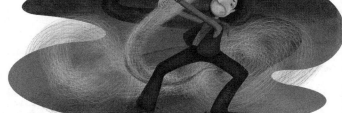

Unit 16 Activity 6
Use after Exercise 3 and Chapter 2

Name _____

Main Idea and Supporting Details

> People say that Pecos Bill was bigger than life. He played with bears and even rode a mountain lion. His whip was a live rattlesnake. Pecos Bill could rope a herd of cattle with one swing of his lasso and then sing songs to settle them down. That Pecos Bill was a superhuman cowboy, or so people say.

1 Who is this paragraph about? _____

2 Supporting Details:
List the details.

- played with bears

- _____
  _____

- _____
  _____

- _____
  _____

3 Write a main idea.
(Start with who the paragraph is about.)

_____
_____
_____
_____
_____

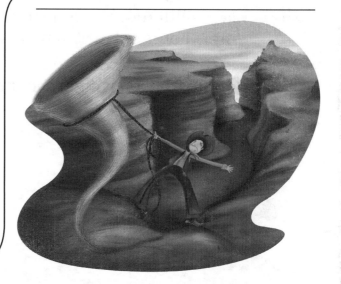

Unit 16 Activity 7
Use after Exercise 4 and Chapter 1

Name _____

Maze Reading

When you come to the words between the parentheses, circle the word that makes the most sense in the paragraph. Then reread the paragraph to see if it makes sense.

Stories say that Slue-Foot Sue lived in Louisiana a long time ago. Sue was a gal with a (very, lot, who) of spunk. She had the courage (but, never, and) energy to do a lot of (easy, difficult, said) things. She roamed all around the (swamp, market, what) in her boat. She was not (tracks, afraid, beautiful) of gators and even wrestled a (bear, run, car).

Characterization

1 Complete the web by writing words or phrases that describe Slue-Foot Sue.

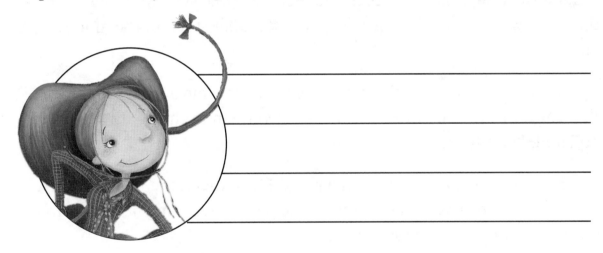

2 Use your web to write a paragraph that describes Sue. Write at least two sentences.

_____

_____

_____

_____

_____

Unit 16 Activity 8
Use after Exercise 4 and Chapter 1

Name _____

Passage Reading Fluency

1. Practice these words:

taught	trouble	giddyup	searched	shallow

2. Read the story 2 times. Cross out a gator each time you read the story.

Sue Saves the Day

Sue's papa taught her to sing like a bird. Then Sue taught herself   13
the songs of the cricket, the gator, and the hoot owl. Soon she was a   28
friend to every animal in the swamp.   35

One cold winter day, Sue heard a call for help. She couldn't see   48
who was in trouble. So Sue sang out to the birds. Then she hummed a   63
song to the tree frogs. Together, they searched the swamp. Finally, in   75
the shallow waters of the river, they found a boat stuck in the muddy   89
bank.   90

Sue called to the people on the boat, "Throw me a rope." With   103
that rope, Sue lassoed three gators and tied them to the boat. Then she   117
hollered, "Giddyup!"   119

Sue drove the boat back to the river. Once there, the boat moved   132
swiftly down the river. Sue waved to the people and sang her songs to   146
thank the animals of the swamp.   152

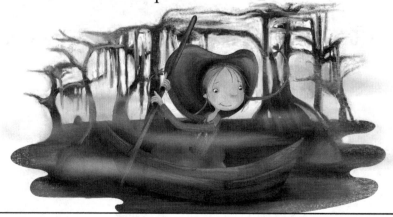

3. Set a timer and see how far you can read in one minute.
   Then cross out the timer.

Unit 16 Activity 9
Use after Exercise 5 and Chapter 2

Name _____

Vocabulary and Alphabetical Order

1. Fill in the missing letters of the alphabet.
2. Find words in your storybook that begin with different letters, and put them in alphabetical order. Two are done for you. Find at least three more.
3. For each word, complete the definition. Then write a sentence using the word.
4. Draw a picture in the box.

A	
E	exaggerate
I	imaginative
O	
U	

challenge • A challenge is something that is

_____

Write a sentence using the word *challenge.*

_____

_____

_____

impossible • Something that is impossible can't

_____

Write a sentence using the word *impossible.*

_____

_____

_____

spunky • Someone who is spunky has the energy to

_____

Write a sentence using the word *spunky.*

_____

_____

_____

Unit 16 Activity 10
Use after Exercise 5 and Chapter 2

Name _____

★ My Tall Tale Character

Describe your own tall tale character by completing the paragraphs below. Have fun making up your own exaggerations and impossible events.

I have a superhuman _____

_____ name is _____
His   Her

_____ is so fast, _____ can _____
She   He   she   he

_____

_____ is also strong.
Name

_____ is so strong, _____ can _____
She   He   she   he

_____

Draw a picture of your tall tale character.

Unit 17 Activity 1
Use after Exercise 1, Links in the Chain, and
From Grass to Meatballs

Name _____

Passage Comprehension
Food Chains

1 **All living things need** _____ **to survive.**

    ○ chains   ○ energy   ○ roast beef

2 **All living things are connected in a food chain.**

   This means they are _____ **in a food chain.**

    ○ lost   ○ looked   ○ linked

3 **The diagram above shows how living things are linked in a food chain.**
Explain how the sun, grass, rabbit, and wolf are connected in a food chain.
Use the word *energy* in your answer.

   First, the sun gives _____

   Then, the rabbit eats _____

   The rabbit gets energy from the grass.

   Finally, the wolf _____

   The wolf gets _____ from the _____

Maze Reading

When you come to the words between the parentheses, circle the word that makes the most sense in the paragraph. Then reread the paragraph to see if it makes sense.

How does grass help people put meatballs on their plates? As strange as it may seem, (grass, plates, are) and meatballs are connected. First, grass (grows, uses, but) energy from the sun to make (food, dogs, fun). Next, cattle eat the grass. Later, (meat, of, cattle) is sold in stores. Finally, people (for, play, buy) the meat, and then it is (used, rabbit, found) to make meatballs.

Sequence • Build a Food Chain

Fill in the blanks to complete the food chain below. Then draw illustrations of each part of your food chain. You may look in your storybook or build a different food chain.

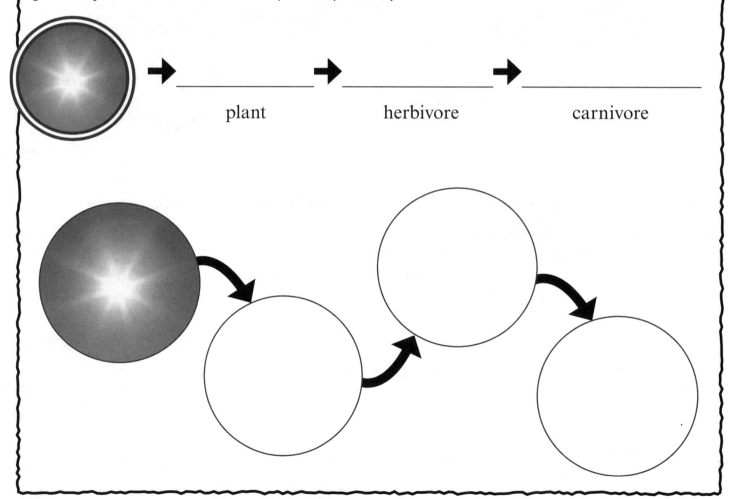

→ _____ → _____ → _____

   plant   herbivore   carnivore

Unit 17 Activity 3
Use after Exercise 2, What's Black and White and
Loved by All? and What's at the Top?

Name _____

Fact Summary
Zebras

1 In this article, you learned that zebras are interesting mammals.
Write facts that support the main idea, "Zebras are interesting mammals."

If you need to, look in your storybook.

Topic/Main Idea: Zebras are interesting mammals.

Fact 1 (page 20)	Fact 2 (page 21)	Fact 3 (page 23)	Fact 4 (page 25)
• are in the _____ family	• have unique _____	• _____ _____ _____	• _____ _____ _____ _____

2 Using at least three of the facts you listed, write a paragraph that tells about
zebras. (Start with *Zebras are interesting mammals . . .*)

_____

_____

_____

_____

_____

_____

_____

Unit 17 Activity 4
Use after Exercise 2, What's Black and White and
Loved by All? and What's at the Top?

Name _____

Passage Comprehension

Lion Facts: Read the sentences and check the box for Yes or No.

	Yes, it is true.	No, it is not true.
Lions are in the cat family.		
Lions are at the top of the food chain.		
Lions are herbivores.		
Lions live in families called prides.		
Lions may sleep as many as 21 hours a day.		

What's Not True?	Yes, it is true.	No, it is not true.
Carnivores love to eat leaves.		
Leaves get energy from the sun.		
Herbivores get energy from leaves.		
Giraffes like to eat the leaves from tall trees.		
Giraffes are carnivores.		
Giraffes give carnivores energy.		
Lions love to eat meat.		
A lion is a predator.		
A lion spends its days grazing on grass.		

Unit 17 Activity 5
Use after Exercise 3, 10 Great Reasons to Be an Earthworm,
and More About the 10 Great Reasons to Be an Earthworm

Name _____

Main Idea and Supporting Details

> Earthworms are important. They make the soil good for growing plants. Here's how. Earthworms eat and digest decaying plants and animals. Then their waste makes the soil rich. Earthworms loosen and mix up the soil when they dig their tunnels. Plants like to grow in rich, loose soil.

1 What is this paragraph about? _____

2 Supporting Details: Earthworms are important because . . .
List the details.

- _____

  _____

  _____

3 Write a main idea. Why are earthworms important?

_____

_____

_____

_____

- _____

  _____

- _____

  _____

Unit 17 Activity 6

Use after Exercise 3, 10 Great Reasons to Be an Earthworm,
and More About the 10 Great Reasons to Be an Earthworm

Name _____

Vocabulary and Alphabetical Order

1. Fill in the missing letters of the alphabet.

★ 2. Find words in your storybook that begin with different letters, and put them in alphabetical order. Two are done for you. Find at least three more.

3. For each word, complete the definition. Then write a sentence using the word.

4. Draw a picture in the box.

C connect

F

H

I

L lion

N

P

R

T

U

W

XYZ

recycle • When you use something again, you

_____

Write a sentence using the word *recycle.*

_____

_____

_____

predator • A **predator** is an animal that hunts other animals for

_____

Write a sentence using the word *predator.*

_____

_____

_____

nomadic • An animal that moves around from place to place is

_____

Write a sentence using the word *nomadic.*

_____

_____

_____

Unit 17 Activity 7
Use after Exercise 4, Digging Up the Truth, and
The Garden We Share, Chapter 1

Name _____

Asking Questions • Letter Writing

Write at least two questions for Professor Worm. You can ask questions about earthworms or other animals in the food chain. Words to help you: Who, What, Where, When, Why, How.

1 **Professor Worm loves to get questions from students around the world. What questions do you have for the squirmy Professor?**

_____

_____

_____

_____

2 **Write a letter to Professor Worm. Introduce yourself and then ask the Professor one or two questions.**

Date:_____

Dear Professor Worm:

_____

_____

_____

_____

_____

_____

_____

Sincerely,

Unit 17 Activity 8
Use after Exercise 4, Digging Up the Truth, and
The Garden We Share, Chapter 1

Name _____

Passage Reading Fluency

1. Practice these words:

oceans	deserts	forests	sand dunes	frozen

2. Read the story 2 times. Cross out chain links each time you read the story.

Food Chains All Around

Thousands of food chains are found around the world—in oceans,	11
deserts, forests, reefs, sand dunes, and ponds. Food chains are found	22
almost everywhere, even where the earth is frozen year round. These	33
food chains are all connected to the sun, and all help to give us energy.	48
The cow is connected to the green grass.	56
The green grass is connected to the sunlight.	64
The sunlight gives plants energy.	69
Oh, see it all around.	74
The fish is connected to the ocean plants.	82
The ocean plants are connected to the sunlight.	90
The sunlight gives plants energy.	95
Oh, see it all around.	100
There are food chains in our world.	107
There are food chains in our world.	114
There are food chains in our world.	121
Oh, see them all around.	126

3. Set a timer and see how far you can read in one minute.
   Then cross out the timer.

Unit 17
Use for fun, as appropriate

Name _____

Just for Fun • Write a Riddle

Write a riddle about an animal, plant, or decomposer. Use the information in the *Science Digest* to write your clues. Write each clue as a question. Don't forget to end each question with a question mark.

Share your riddle with your family and friends. See if they can guess the answer.

Clue 1: **What** _____

_____

Clue 2: **What** _____

_____

Clue 3: **What** _____

_____

Answer: _____

Illustrate your answer.

Unit 17 Activity 9
Use after Exercise 5 and The Garden We Share,
Chapters 2 and 3

Name _____

Story Map
The Garden We Share

If you need to, look in your storybook.

◆ INTRODUCTION

Setting	**Where**

Narrator	**Who**

● BEGINNING

Initiating Event **Problem**	

Goal	**Cara's Plan**

■ MIDDLE

Action	**Neighbors** _____
	Garden
	Aphid Problem/Solution
	Rabbit Problem/Solution

▲ END

Outcome/ Conclusion	• _____

Unit 17 Activity 10a
Use after Exercise 5 and The Garden We Share,
Chapters 2 and 3

Name _____

Written Retell
The Garden We Share

◆ **INTRODUCTION • Setting/Narrator**
   Tell where the story takes place and who is telling the story.

_____

_____

_____

_____

● **BEGINNING • Initiating Event:** Describe the problem and the narrator's goal.

_____

_____

_____

_____

■ **MIDDLE • Action**
   Write what the neighbors did to the vacant lot. Describe the garden.
   Explain how the aphid and rabbit problems were solved.

First, _____

_____

_____

Soon the garden _____

_____

_____

Unit 17 Activity 10b
Use after Activity 10a

Name _____

One day, the neighbors found tiny aphids _____

_____

_____

The rabbits liked the garden too! _____

_____

_____

▲ **END • Outcome/Conclusion:** Write what happened at the end.

_____

_____

_____

_____

STORY RESPONSE Start with *I liked the story because . . .* or *I didn't like the story because . . .*

_____

_____

ILLUSTRATION Draw a picture of your favorite part of the story.

✓ **Check and Correct**
Read your story retell.

Do your sentences make sense? ☐
Do the sentences tell the story? ☐
Do you have a capital at the beginning of each sentence and a period at the end? ☐
Did you use your best handwriting? ☐

Unit 18 Activity 1
Use after Exercise 1 and Chapters 1 and 2

Name _____

Passage Comprehension
The Great Barrier Reef

1 **Open your storybook to page 9. Look at the photo of Earth from space. Why is <u>Earth</u> called the blue planet?**

_____

_____

_____

2 **The Great Barrier Reef is . . .**

     ○ an island.   ○ a continent.   ○ hundreds of coral reefs and islands.

3 **An ecosystem is a community of animals and plants living together.**

The Great Barrier Reef is an example of an _____

4 **Complete the captions below.** The Great Barrier Reef is home to . . .

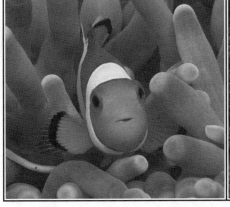  

about 1,500 types of _____	_____ 5,000 types of mollusks	approximately _____ types of hard coral

5 **A snazzy word for *about* and *around* is** _____

Unit 18 Activity 2
Use after Exercise 1 and Chapters 1 and 2

Name _____

Passage Comprehension • Build a Food Chain
Food Chains in the Reef

1 **A snazzy word for meat eater is** _____

2 **A snazzy word for plant eater is** _____

3 **A snazzy word for an animal that eats plants and meat is**

_____

4 **Like _all_ food chains, the food chains in the Great Barrier Reef start with energy from the . . .**

       O food.   O sun.   O animals.

5 **Look in your storybook on pages 14 and 15. Draw pictures to complete the food chain.**

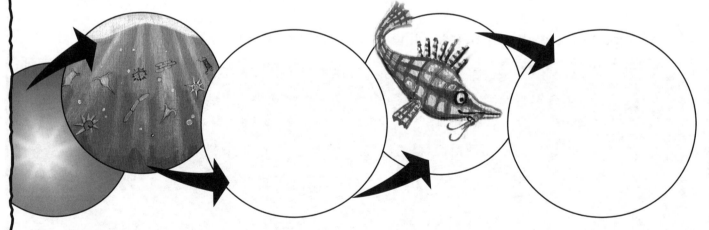

6 **Fill in the blanks to complete this food chain.**

Sunlight is soaked up by little plants called phytoplankton. Shrimp eat the

_____. Longnose hawkfish eat the

_____. Finally, a _____ eats the longnose

hawkfish. The _____ is at the top of the food chain.

Name _____

Story Comprehension
Miss Tam at the Great Barrier Reef

1 **Where does the story take place?**

_____

_____

2 **It was funny to imagine Miss Tam . . .**

○ squeezing into a wetsuit.   ○ going to the Great Barrier Reef.

3 **Write two or more sentences that tell what you think about Miss Tam and why.**

I _____ Miss Tam because _____
    like   do not like

_____

_____ | face mask |

_____ | _____ |

4 **Look at Miss Tam. Label her diving equipment.**
The first one has been done for you.

- face mask
- weight belt
- inflatable vest
- air tank
- fins

Name _____

Story Map
Miss Tam at the Great Barrier Reef

◆ INTRODUCTION

| Setting | **Where** |

| Main Character | Miss Tam _____ _____ _____ |

● BEGINNING

| Initiating Event **Goal** | • _____ |

■ MIDDLE

| Action | • went on a boat to the reef
• put on _____
• saw _____
_____
_____
_____
_____ |

▲ END

| Outcome/ Conclusion | • _____
• _____ |

Unit 18 Activity 5a
Use after Exercise 3 and Chapters 1 and 2

Name _____

Written Retell
Miss Tam at the Great Barrier Reef

◆ **INTRODUCTION** • **Setting/Main Character:** Tell where the story takes place and who the main character is. Write at least two sentences.

_____

_____

_____

● **BEGINNING** • **Initiating Event:** Write what happened at the beginning of the story.

_____

_____

_____

_____

■ **MIDDLE** • **Action:** Write what Miss Tam did at the Great Barrier Reef.

First, Miss Tam went on a boat to the Great Barrier Reef.

Next, _____

_____

_____

_____

_____

continued ➡

Unit 18 Activity 5b
Use after Exercise 3 and Chapters 1 and 2

Name _____

Then, _____

_____

_____

_____

▲ **END • Outcome/Conclusion:** Write what happened at the end. You may wish to tell about how you think Miss Tam felt at the end of the story.

At the end, _____

_____

_____

_____

ILLUSTRATION Draw a picture of your favorite part of the story.

✓ Check
and Correct

Read your story retell.

1. Do your sentences make sense? ☐

2. Do the sentences tell the story? ☐

3. Do you have a capital at the beginning of each sentence and a period at the end? ☐

4. Did you use your best handwriting? ☐

Unit 18
For use anytime after Chapter 2

Name _____

Just for Fun • If I Were . . .

1 If you could be an animal on the Great Barrier Reef, which animal would you choose to be?

Octopus

Coral Polyp

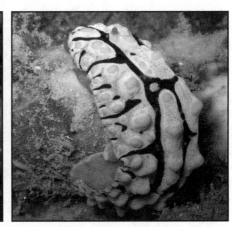
Nudibranch

2 Use at least one fact to explain why you chose this animal.

I would want to be a _____ because

_____

_____

_____

_____

3 Draw a picture of yourself as a

_____

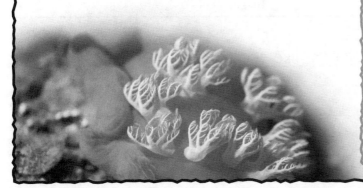

Pete the Pufferfish

Name _____

Setting Web
Reef Community

1 **Setting:** Where does <u>Pete</u> live?

_____

_____

2 **Web:** Write words or phrases that describe where Pete lives. Use what you've learned about coral reefs.

The Great Barrier Reef is:
(pages 10 and 11)

near Australia
_____
_____
_____

Animals of the Great Barrier Reef are:
(pages 11–19)

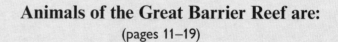

mollusks, like sea slugs
_____
_____

Unit 18 Activity 7
Use after Exercise 4 and Chapters 1 and 2

Name _____

Passage Reading Fluency

1. Practice these words:

| approximately | polyp | 5,000 | 360 | ancient | mollusks |

2. Read the story 2 times. Cross out a letter each time you read the story.

A Letter From Pete

Dear Mom,   2

   I am fine. I'm living on the Great Barrier Reef. It's beautiful here,   15
and I have lots of new friends. Mother Octopus and Grandfather Sea   27
Turtle watch out for me.   32

   A lot of us live here—around 1,500 types of fish! There are   45
approximately 5,000 types of mollusks and about 360 types of coral.   56

   Grandfather Turtle says the Great Barrier Reef is ancient. He says   67
the coral polyps have been building the reef for thousands of years. He   80
says the little polyps build hard skeletons around themselves and then   91
leave the skeletons behind.   95

   I like the reef. It's awesome. It's splendid. It's wonderful.   105

                    Love,   106
                    Pete   107

3. Set a timer and see how far you can read in one minute.
   Then cross out the timer.

Name _____

Snazzy Words and Sophisticated Sentences

Pete the Pufferfish is a lot of fun. The authors made the story come alive by choosing interesting words. Read the sentences below. For each sentence pair, select the snazziest and most grown-up, or sophisticated, sentence. The word choices are underlined.

Chapter 1:

    ○ Once at the big reef, Pete was amazed by all the <u>commotion</u>.

    ○ Once at the big reef, Pete was amazed by all the <u>noise and activity</u>.

Chapter 2:

    ○ The <u>very old</u> turtle shrugged his flippers.

    ○ The <u>ancient</u> turtle shrugged his flippers.

Chapter 3:

    ○ Ink will allow you to escape from a hungry <u>predator</u>.

    ○ Ink will allow you to escape from a hungry <u>hunter</u>.

Chapter 4:

    ○ Mother Octopus had <u>told</u> Lady Ann the Seahorse to come.

    ○ Mother Octopus had <u>summoned</u> Lady Ann the Seahorse.

    ○ Despite all of his <u>contortions</u>, his color didn't change.

    ○ Despite all of his <u>wiggling around</u>, his color didn't change.

Snazzy Words and Synonyms

Draw a line from the words that mean the same or almost the same thing.

commotion •	• very old
ancient •	• wiggling around
summoned •	• noise and activity
contortions •	• told

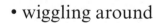

Pete the Pufferfish

Name _____

Characterization
Pete the Pufferfish

1 **Which three words describe Pete?**

○ determined   ○ spunky

○ ravenous   ○ an herbivore

○ extinct   ○ an omnivore

2 **Use two words from above to describe Pete. Explain why the words you chose describe Pete.**
One is done for you.

Pete was ___determined___. He showed he was ___determined___

by _trying many ways to protect himself. He didn't give up._

Pete was ___an omnivore___. We know he was an omnivore because

_____

_____

3 **What do you think about Pete?**

I _____ Pete because _____
    like   do not like

_____

_____

_____

_____

_____

Unit 18
Use anytime after Chapter 4

Name _____

𝒥ust for 𝒻un • Authors' Corner

Jessica Sprick began writing stories for *Read Well* when she was ten years old. Her first story was "Jag and Panther." She wrote her second *Read Well* story, "Why the Sloth Is Slow," when she was eighteen.

"Pete the Pufferfish" was written by Jessica and her mom, Marilyn Sprick. Since Jessica was very little, she and her mom have been writing stories together. Jessica often starts the story. She has great ideas! Then she and her mom pass the story back and forth. When it sounds just right, they sit back and smile.

Now Jessica is a teacher. When she was twenty-two years old, she went on an African adventure. She taught math and science in a small village in Ghana for four months. Can you guess what other story she wrote for *Read Well 2?*

If you could meet Jessica, what would you ask her?

How _____

_____

Why _____

_____

What _____

_____

> Answer: Jessica wrote "Miss Tam Goes to Africa." Kwesi is the name of Jessica's professor. The real Kwesi immigrated to the United States. He teaches music at the University of Colorado.

Entry
1
(1 of 2)

My Book Journal

Cover art by: _____

Title of book: _____

Author: _____

Illustrator: _____

(Teachers: If you are using the Activity Book, tear out and staple pages 73 to 80 to make a separate Book Journal.)

Entry
1
(2 of 2)

Chapter 1
The Big Bulletin Board

1 **Who is the main character?** _____

2 **Draw a picture of Flat Stanley in the circle. Then write words that describe him.**

If I woke up as flat as a pancake, I would . . .

Try to use a snazzy word: **distressed speechless amazed**

_____

_____

Write two things you would do if you were as flat as a pancake. Write at least one sentence.

_____

_____

_____

✓ Check and Correct

Read your answers. Do your answers make sense? ☐
Did you use your best handwriting? ☐

Entry
2

Chapter 2
Being Flat

I think traveling in an envelope would be _____

_____

It would be _____ because

_____

_____

_____

I would go to _____

because _____

_____

_____

Try to use a
snazzy word:
**adventure
round-trip
eventful
fascinating
unique**

Draw a picture of yourself being mailed to _____

Chapter 3
Stanley the Kite

How does Arthur feel about Stanley the kite?
- ○ Arthur is jealous of Stanley.
- ○ Arthur is happy with Stanley.
- ○ Arthur feels sorry for Stanley.

If I could fly like a kite, I would have a bird's-eye view.

I could _____

_____

_____

_____

I _____ this part of the chapter because
      liked   did not like

_____

_____

_____

_____

Entry
4

Chapter 4
The Museum Thieves
(pages 35–45)

Would you want to be disguised as a shepherdess?

     yes   no

If I had to wear a disguise and stand in a picture frame, I

would choose to be a _____

because _____

_____

_____

Try to use a snazzy word:
recognize
sensational

Draw a picture of what you would look like in the frame.

Entry
5

Chapter 4

The Museum Thieves

(pages 46–54)

I was impressed by Stanley because _____

_____

_____

_____

_____

_____

I _____ to be Flat Stanley because
   would like   would not like

_____

_____

_____

_____

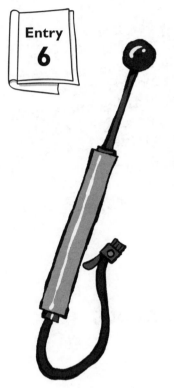

Entry 6

Chapter 5
Arthur's Good Idea

Stanley had many adventures. The one I like best was

_____

_____

because _____

_____

_____

_____

Would you recommend this book to other kids your age?   yes   no

What would you tell a friend about this book? _____

_____

Would you like to read more books about Flat Stanley?   yes   no

What question would you like to ask the author, Jeff Brown?

_____

_____

_____

_____

Visit the library. If you enjoyed Flat Stanley, you may want to read more about his amazing adventures. Read all about Stanley and a genie; his trip in a spaceship; becoming invisible; and Stanley, flat again.

Have fun.

Other stories you might like to read about Flat Stanley

Stanley and the Magic Lamp by Jeff Brown

Fiction • Imaginative

Stanley finds a magic lamp with a real genie inside. The genie is happy to grant Stanley everything he wishes for. Stanley finds that getting everything he wants can be a headache.

Stanley in Space by Jeff Brown

Fiction • Imaginative

Stanley and his family are selected by the president of the United States to take off in the Star Scout, a top-secret spaceship.

Invisible Stanley by Jeff Brown

Fiction • Imaginative

After an electrical storm, Stanley wakes up invisible. He finds all sorts of ways to help out with his new talent. But will we ever see Stanley again?

Stanley, Flat Again by Jeff Brown

Fiction • Imaginative

Stanley deflates again after his brother Arthur hits him with a tennis ball. The bicycle pump doesn't work this time, so Stanley embarks on a new round of flat adventures.

Unit 19 Activity 1
Use after Exercise 1 and Chapter 1

Name _____

Story Comprehension
The Big Bulletin Board

1 **At the beginning of the chapter, the author introduced us to Stanley Lambchop. Stanley Lambchop is . . .**

Check all correct descriptions.

___ the main character.

___ the boy who became flat.

___ the owner of a dog named Lambchop.

___ Arthur's older brother.

2 **Cause and Effect: Complete the box to tell how Stanley became flat.**

Action/Cause		Outcome/Effect: What happened to Stanley?
A huge _____ _____ fell on Stanley.	→	_____ _____

3 **Mrs. Lambchop took Stanley to the doctor. The doctor said Stanley needed to . . .**

○ take medicine.   ○ be watched.   ○ stay home.

4 **The nurse took Stanley's measurements. Stanley is . . .**

• _____ feet tall

• about a foot wide

• half an inch _____

Look at the ruler. Find the mark for half an inch. That is how thick Stanley is.

Unit 19 Activity 2
Use after Exercise 2 and Chapter 2

Name _____

Story Comprehension • Main Idea

Complete the main idea. Then list three supporting details that tell what Stanley could do because he was flat. The first one is done for you.

Topic/Main Idea: _____ could do many extraordinary things because he was flat.

Supporting Details

- slide under the door
- _____
- _____

Maze Reading
The Next Best Thing

When you come to the words between the parentheses, circle the word that makes the most sense in the paragraph. Then reread the paragraph to see if it makes sense.

Coral's Aunt Tam lived clear across the country. Coral missed her and wanted to (visit, play, plane), but it was too expensive to (jostle, bed, buy) a plane ticket.

Coral thought, "If (enormous, I, he) were flat like Stanley, I could (swim, train, travel) across the country in an envelope." (Stanley, Could, Coral) decided to do the next best (want, thing, gift). She decided to write a letter (in, hurry, to) Aunt Tam. Coral told her aunt (about, by, drew) going to the dinosaur museum. She (colored, told, special) her about the book she was (hiding, reading, expensive). She even drew a picture of herself. Finally, Coral mailed her letter.

Name _____

Vocabulary ★ Absurd

Flat Stanley

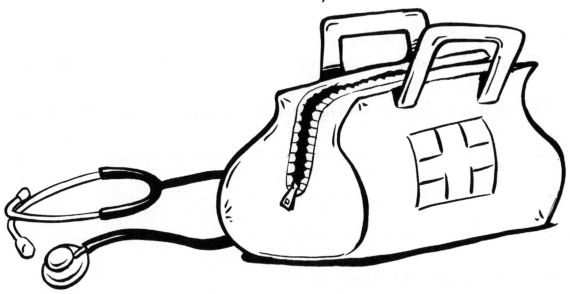

The author created an *absurd* character and absurd events. When someone or something is absurd, it is unbelievable! Read the sentences, and circle "yes" or "no." What makes Stanley an absurd character?

1 **Stanley was flattened by a bulletin board.**

    Is that absurd?   yes   no

2 **Stanley went to the doctor.**

    Is that absurd?   yes   no

3 **Stanley was half an inch thick.**

    Is that absurd?   yes   no

4 **Stanley was invited to visit his friend in California.**

    Is that absurd?   yes   no

5 **Stanley was mailed in an envelope to his friend's house.**

    Is that absurd?   yes   no

Check and Correct: "Yes" should be circled three times.

Unit 19 Activity 4
Use after Exercise 4 and Chapter 4, pages 35–45

Name _____

Story Comprehension
The Museum Thieves, pages 35–45

1 **Mr. Dart is the director of the . . .**

    ○ Famous Museum of Dinosaurs.   ○ Famous Museum of Art.

2 **Mr. Dart was ordinarily a cheerful person. Why did <u>Mr. Dart</u> become gloomy?**

_____

_____

_____

3 **What did <u>Mr. Dart</u> want Stanley to do?**

_____

_____

_____

    ○ Mr. Dart wanted Stanley to wear a shepherdess disguise and stand in a picture frame.

    ○ Mr. Dart wanted Stanley to put himself into an envelope and mail himself to the thieves.

    ○ Mr. Dart wanted Stanley to put on a disguise and smile at the sheep.

Unit 19 Activity 5
Use after Exercise 5 and Chapter 4, pages 46–54

Name _____

Story Comprehension • Sequence of Events
The Museum Thieves, pages 46–54

1 **Setting:** **Where did *most* of this chapter take place?**

○ in the park   ○ in the museum   ○ in California

2 **Sequence of Events: Fill in the chart to show what happened in Chapter 4.**

3 **Using your list of events, write what happened in Chapter 4.**

First Event

Mr. Dart was gloomy because

paintings were being

_____

↓

Next Event

Stanley helped Mr. Dart. He

put on a _____

and hid in a _____

↓

Next Event

Stanley waited in the painting

and helped to catch the

_____

↓

Conclusion

Stanley was a hero and

got a _____

At the beginning of the chapter, Mr. Dart was gloomy because

_____

_____

_____

Next, Stanley helped Mr. Dart by

_____

_____

_____

Then, _____

_____

_____

Finally, _____

_____

_____

Unit 19 Activity 6
Use after Exercise 6 and Chapter 5

Name _____

Crossword Puzzle
Flat Stanley

Fill in the blanks using words from the word bank. Use the words from the word bank to complete the crossword puzzle.

Down

1. We _____ read a book about Flat Stanley.

2. He was _____ because he was flat as a pancake.

3. *Flat Stanley* has many unbelievable or _____ events.

Across

4. Stanley became famous when he helped catch the museum thieves.

   The story was _____.

5. Stanley wore a _____ and dressed like a shepherdess.

6. Stanley had to _____ his looks so the thieves wouldn't see him.

Word Bank

disguise
sensational
alter
absurd
recently
unique

		1 r								
4 s	e	n	s	a	t	i	o	n	3 a	l
		c							b	
		e		5 d	i	s	g	2 u	i	s	e
		n						n	u	
		t						i	r	
6 a	l	t	e	r				q	d	
		y						u		
								e		

Name _____

Story Comprehension
pages 4–7

1 Ms. Frizzle's class is going to a _____ museum.

2 The class is going to learn about the _____

○ dinosaurs   ○ human body   ○ school bus

3 Write facts that support the main idea.

If you need to, look in your storybook on pages 6 and 7.

Topic/Main Idea: Your <u>body</u> is made of cells.

Fact 1 (page 6)	**Fact 2** (page 6)	**Fact 3** (page 7)	**Fact 4** (page 7)
• _____ of cells	• can't be seen without a _____	• need _____	• have different _____

4 Using the facts you've listed, write a paragraph about cells. Start with the main idea. Then write at least three supporting details.

Your body is made of cells. _____

_____

_____

_____

_____

_____

Name _____

Fact Sheet

Complete the title with a snazzy word. Add your name as the author.
Complete the illustrations of the cells. See page 7 in your storybook.

Next, select one type of cell. Then complete the sentence at the bottom of the page.
Draw a picture to show you and these cells at work.

Cells Are _____

by _____

Lung Cells	Muscle Cells	Brain Cells
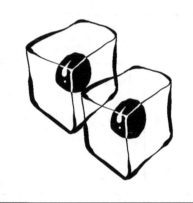		

_____ cells help you _____

The Human Body

by _____

(Teachers: If you are using the Activity Book, tear out and staple pages 89 to 92 to make a separate folder.)

Unit 20

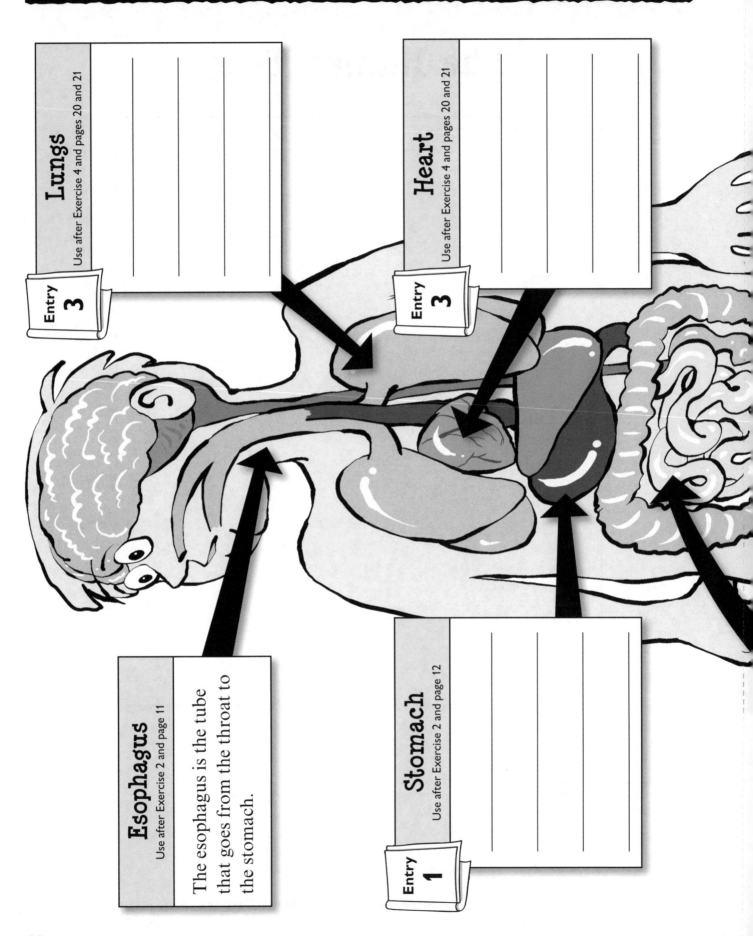

Lungs
Use after Exercise 4 and pages 20 and 21

Entry
3

Heart
Use after Exercise 4 and pages 20 and 21

Entry
3

Esophagus
Use after Exercise 2 and page 11

The esophagus is the tube that goes from the throat to the stomach.

Stomach
Use after Exercise 2 and page 12

Entry
1

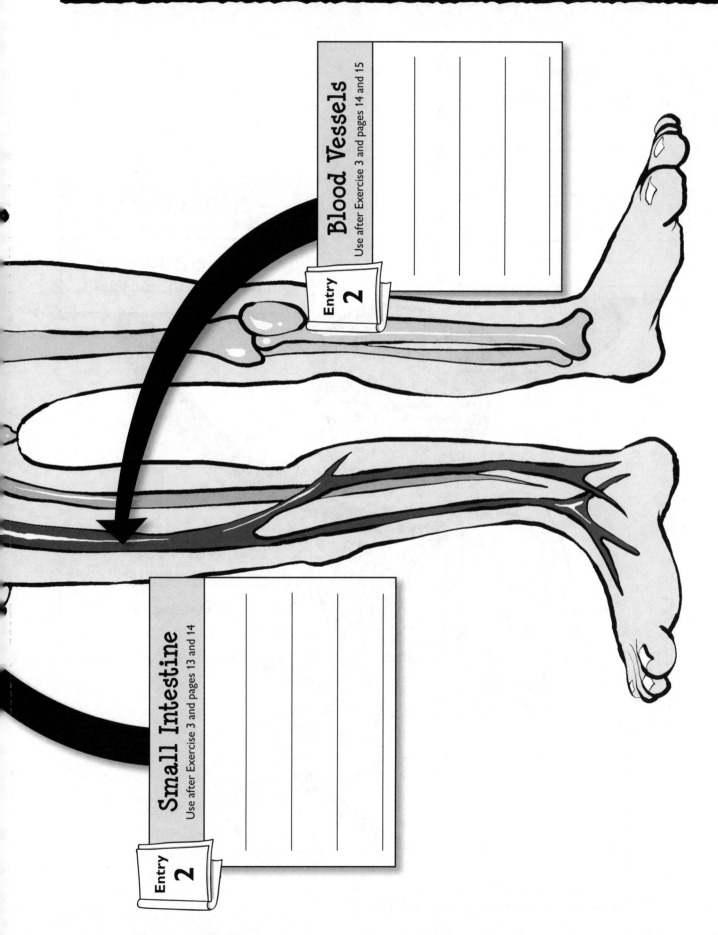

Blood Vessels
Use after Exercise 3 and pages 14 and 15

Entry
2

Small Intestine
Use after Exercise 3 and pages 13 and 14

Entry
2

Unit 20

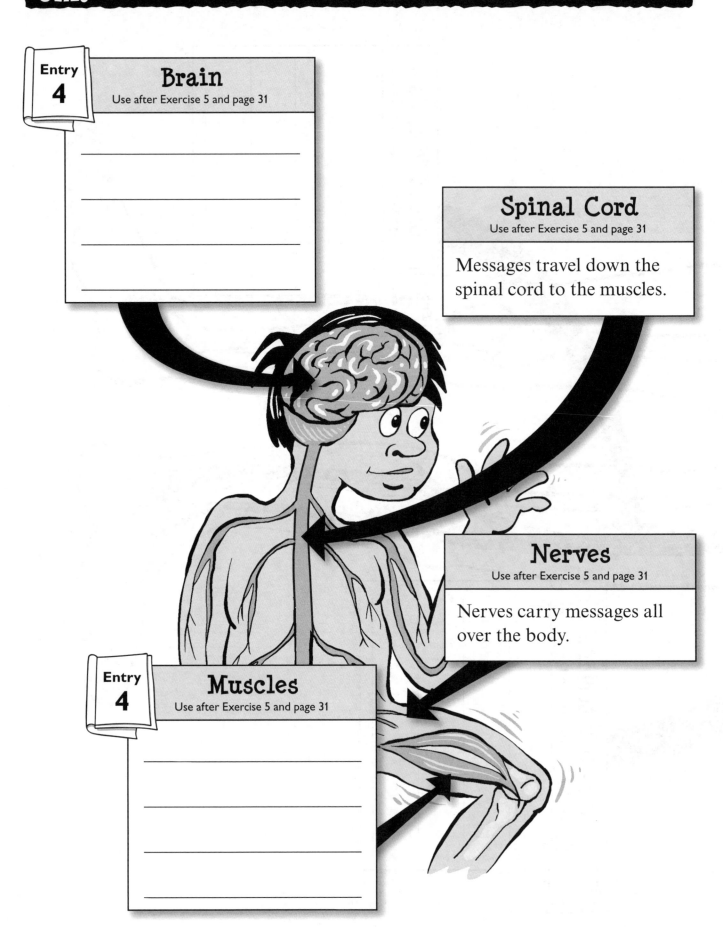

Entry 4

Brain
Use after Exercise 5 and page 31

_____

_____

_____

_____

Spinal Cord
Use after Exercise 5 and page 31

Messages travel down the spinal cord to the muscles.

Nerves
Use after Exercise 5 and page 31

Nerves carry messages all over the body.

Entry 4

Muscles
Use after Exercise 5 and page 31

_____

_____

_____

Unit 20 Activity 3
Use after Exercise 2 and pages 8–13

Name _____

Story Comprehension
pages 8–13

1 **After stopping at the park for lunch, who missed getting back on the bus?**

    ○ Greg   ○ Arnold   ○ Ms. Frizzle

2 **How can you tell that Arnold ate the bus?** Look at page 10 in your storybook.

   • First the bus _____

   • Arnold had a handful of Cheesie-Weesies.

     The bus landed in Arnold's _____

   • Arnold ate the Cheesie-Weesies and _____

3 **The school bus ended up . . .**

    ○ at the park.   ○ inside Arnold.   ○ at the museum.

Maze Reading

When you come to the words between the parentheses, circle the word that makes the most sense in the paragraph. Then reread the paragraph to see if it makes sense.

> The esophagus is the tube that goes from the mouth to the stomach. Muscles along the esophagus push the (food, Arnold, run) down to the stomach.
>
> In the (eating, esophagus, stomach), the food is mashed and churned. (Then, bird, before) food is digested and becomes a (thin, thick, sleep) liquid. Then it goes to the (large, small, man) intestine.

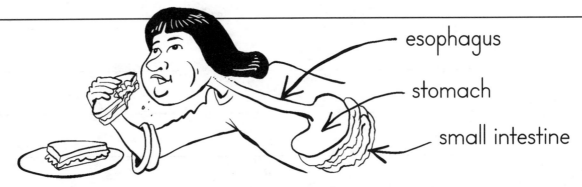

esophagus

stomach

small intestine

The Magic School Bus: Inside the Human Body

Unit 20 Activity 4
Use after Exercise 3 and Chapters 14–19

Name _____

Story Comprehension
pages 14–19

1 The magic school bus went from Arnold's:

a. mouth

b. esophagus

c. _____

d. small _____

2 Label the diagram.

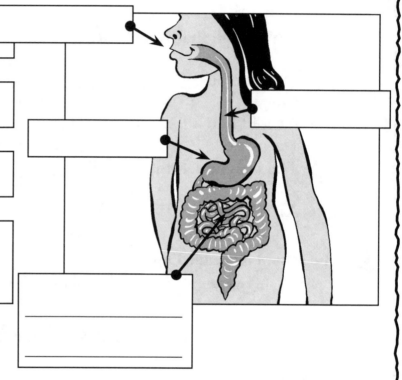

3 What are blood vessels? Blood vessels are tubes that _____

_____

○ bring water to your body   ○ carry blood through your body

4 **Main Idea: Blood is important to our bodies.** List two supporting details that tell why blood is important. If you need to, look back in your book on pages 16–17.

• _____

_____

• _____

_____

94

©2009 Sopris West Educational Services. All Rights Reserved.

Unit 20 Extra Fluency Passage
Use after Exercise 4 and pages 20–23 (optional)

Name _____

Passage Reading Fluency

1. Practice these words:

| usually | imaginative | human | exhausted | impossible |

2. Read the story 2 times. Cross out a sleeping cat each time you read the story.

Sleep

At night, it is time for our brains and bodies to rest. People who   14
try to go without sleep become exhausted. They don't remember very   25
well and have a hard time learning new things. Have you ever tried   38
to stay up past your bedtime? What happens? You always fall asleep   50
sooner or later. The human body needs rest.   58

There are 24 hours in a day. You should sleep at least 8 hours every   73
day. That means you will spend one third of your life sleeping! If you   87
live to be 75 years old, you will spend 25 years asleep!   99

What happens when you sleep? You go through several stages of   110
sleep. You have deep sleep and light sleep, and you dream. No one   123
knows why we dream. Dreams can be fun. Sometimes we see ourselves   135
doing impossible things, like flying through the air or swimming like   146
a fish. We usually forget our dreams quickly. People who like to write   159
imaginative stories sometimes write down their dreams as soon as they   170
wake up in the morning. Try it! Your dream might make a great story.   184

3. Set a timer and see how far you can read in one minute.
   Then cross out the timer.

Unit 20 Activity 5
Use after Exercise 4 and pages 20–23

Name _____

Vocabulary and Alphabetical Order

A

C

digestion

E

intestine

O

1. Fill in the missing letters of the alphabet.

2. Find words in your storybook that begin with different letters, and put them in alphabetical order. Two are done for you. Find at least three more.

3. For each word, complete the definition. Then write a sentence using the word.

4. Draw a picture in the box.

experiment • An experiment is _____

_____

Write a sentence using the word *experiment.*

_____

_____

glimpse • When you take a glimpse at something, you

_____

Write a sentence using the word *glimpse.*

_____

_____

oxygen • Oxygen _____

_____

Complete the sentence

We need oxygen to . . .

_____

96

Unit 20 Activity 6
Use after Exercise 5 and pages 24–31

Name _____

Story Comprehension • Cause and Effect
pages 24–31

Fill in the blanks with words from the word bank. When you use a word, cross it out. Each row shows what made something happen.

Word Bank

brain	esophagus	nose	panic
pound	school	stomach	sneeze

Cause: Event

The bus traveled down a dark tunnel. The bus was in Arnold's

_____

➤

Effect: What happened?

Arnold didn't feel well because the bus traveled from his esophagus into his

_____

Cause: Event

Arnold realized he was lost and

began to _____

_____

➤

Effect: What happened?

His brain needed oxygen so he could think. His heart began to

_____

Cause: Event

Arnold's heart pumped red blood cells to the lungs. The blood was circulated to Arnold's

_____

➤

Effect: What happened?

The red blood cells took oxygen to Arnold's brain, so he could think better. Arnold figured out how to get back to

_____

Cause: Event

The bus ended up in Arnold's

_____

➤

Effect: What happened?

This made Arnold

_____

Unit 20
Use anytime after pages 32–37

Name _____

Just for Fun • Visualizing and Illustrating
My Favorite Organ

Which is your favorite organ? Write at least two sentences and draw a picture. Look at the bird next to your poster. What do you think she could be saying? Write a caption in her speech bubble.

My Favorite Organ

by _____

Name _____

Date _____

The Water Spider

Note
- Before beginning the assessment, have students read the title.
  Have students read the warm-up words in the box on the next page.
- Then have students complete the assessment on their own.

WARM-UP

pond	underwater	swimmers	attacks	survive

The Water Spider

Water spiders spend most of their lives under the water. All spiders breathe air, so how does the water spider survive? This is how. First, it spins a silk house on an underwater plant. Next, the spider goes to the surface. It uses small hairs on its abdomen to trap air. The spider carries the air in small bubbles to its house and puts them inside. Now the spider has air to breathe in its house.

The water spider is a carnivore. It eats insects. When an insect is near, the spider zips out and attacks. It takes the insect back to its house and has a nice meal.

Water spiders also lay their eggs in their silk homes. They even raise their babies there. The silk house is a safe place.

The water spider lives, hunts, eats, and raises its babies in a pond. It's no surprise! These spiders are great swimmers.

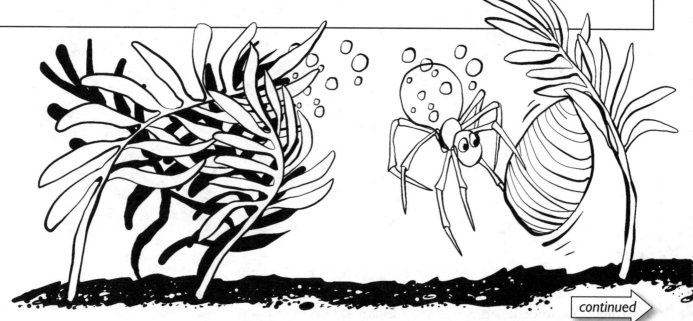

continued

TOPIC

1 **This passage is about . . .**

     ○ water spiders.

     ○ spiders.

     ○ silk houses.

NOTE TAKING, FACTS

2 **Note taking: Write four facts about water spiders.**

  Topic: Water Spiders

    Fact 1: spend most of their lives _____

    Fact 2: spin _____

    _____

    Fact 3: _____

    _____

    Fact 4: _____

    _____

MAIN IDEA

3 **Complete the main idea sentence. Water spiders . . .**

     ○ live underwater only when they are babies.

     ○ breathe underwater only at night.

     ○ spend most of their lives underwater.

Turn the page.

VOCABULARY

4 The story says that the water spider's silk house is a safe place for the spider

babies. The water spider babies are _____ from harm.

    ○ obeyed   ○ protected   ○ valuable

SEQUENCE OF EVENTS

5 **Complete the sentences to tell how a water spider survives underwater.**

First, the spider spins a silk house on an _____

Next, the spider goes _____

Then the spider carries small bubbles of air to _____

_____

At last, the water spider can breathe in its underwater home.

✓ Check
and Correct →

Reread your answers.
Do your answers make sense? ☐
Do you have a capital at the beginning of each sentence
    and a period at the end? ☐
Did you use your best handwriting? ☐

SCORING   Date _____

Topic ___ /1	Note Taking, Facts ___ /4	Main Idea ___ /1
Vocabulary ___ /1	Sequence of Events ___ /3	Total ___ /10

Teachers: If you wish to keep a cumulative record of student assessment scores, see the *Assessment Manual.*

Name _____

Date _____

Growing Up as a Little Brown Bat

Note

• Before beginning the assessment, have students read the title.
  Have students read the warm-up words in the box on the next page.
• Then have students complete the assessment on their own.

WARM-UP

| nursery | mosquitoes | billowy | ceiling | special |

Growing Up as a Little Brown Bat

I'm a little brown bat. When I was born, I had no hair on my body. I couldn't see because my eyes were closed. I stayed real close to my mother. When she went hunting, I hung onto her tightly as she sailed through the night air grabbing mosquitoes.

My eyes opened two days after I was born. I saw that I was in a dark cave with thousands of other mothers and baby bats. It was a bat nursery! Soon I was old enough to stay with the other baby bats while my mother went hunting. She and I had special calls so we could find each other when she returned.

I drank my mother's milk and grew fast. When I was four weeks old, I was as big as she was. One day I let go of the ceiling and flapped my billowy wings. I could fly! My mother showed me how to catch insects. Soon I was able to take care of myself.

continued

TOPIC

1 **What is this passage about?**

This passage is about _____

NOTE TAKING, FACTS

2 **Note taking: Write three facts that tell about little brown bat babies.**

When little brown bats are babies, they . . .

Fact 1: have no _____

Fact 2: _____

Fact 3: _____

VOCABULARY

3 **In Unit 14, you learned that bats are . . .**
   ○ birds.   ○ mammals.   ○ arachnids.

SUPPORTING DETAILS

4 **Check two ways mother bats take care of their babies. Mother bats . . .**
   __ sing songs to their babies.
   __ hunt for food for their babies.
   __ teach their babies how to catch insects.
   __ rock their babies to sleep.

VOCABULARY—CARNIVORES

5 **What words in the story tell you that bats are *carnivores*?**
   ○ "I let got of the ceiling and flapped my billowy wings."
   ○ "I stayed close to my mother."
   ○ "My mother showed me how to catch insects."

Turn the page.

SEQUENCE OF EVENTS

6 **Describe how a baby bat grows up.**

First, the baby bat was born. It stayed with its mother.

Next, the little brown bat stayed in a nursery with other little brown bats.

Then, _____

_____

Finally, _____

✔ Check
and Correct

Reread your answers.

Do your answers make sense? ☐

Do you have a capital at the beginning of each sentence
and a period at the end? ☐

Did you use your best handwriting? ☐

SCORING   Date _____

Topic ___/1	Note Taking, Facts ___/3	Vocabulary ___/1	
Supporting Details ___/2	Vocabulary ___/1	Sequence of Events ___/2	Total ___/10

Teachers: If you wish to keep a cumulative record of student assessment scores, see the *Assessment Manual.*

Name _____

Date _____

The Pony Express

Note
- Before beginning the assessment, have students read the title.
  Have students read the warm-up words in the box on the next page.
- Then have students complete the assessment on their own.

WARM-UP

stagecoach	Missouri	Charlie	invented	machines

The Pony Express

People who went West in the 1800s needed ways to stay in touch with their families in the East. There were no cars or planes. There were no phones. Mail was sent by stagecoach or boat. It could take six months for mail to get from coast to coast. Often it was lost along the way.

In 1860, the Pony Express was started. Young men carried the mail on horses. They rode fast. It took just ten days to get mail from Missouri to the West Coast. Every ten miles, riders would stop and get a fresh horse. Every hundred miles, the riders would pass the mail to the next rider. This way, the men and horses would have time to rest. One of the youngest riders was a boy named Charlie. He was only eleven years old!

The Pony Express worked well. But it lasted for only about a year and a half. What happened? New machines were invented. News could travel from coast to coast in minutes. The Pony Express was no longer needed.

continued

TOPIC

1 **What is this passage about?**

This passage is about _____

GOAL, VOCABULARY

2 **People in the West needed ways to stay in touch with their families in the East. What did they want to do?**

___ They wanted to travel by plane to visit their families.

___ They wanted to communicate with their families in the East.

___ They wanted to draw pictures of the West for their families.

SUPPORTING DETAILS, CHART

3 **Topic: Pony Express . . .**

Fill in the supporting details in the box.

• started in the year _____

• carried mail _____

• riders passed the mail to _____

_____

• took ten days to get mail from

_____

_____

MAIN IDEA, CHART

4 **What is the main idea?**

The Pony Express _____

_____

_____

_____

_____

_____

○ made it easier for people to communicate from coast to coast.

○ used horses.

○ lasted a year and a half.

Turn the page.

DRAWING CONCLUSIONS

5 **The Pony Express lasted only a year and a half. Why?**

　○ The Pony Express riders were faster than the new machines.

　○ The Pony Express riders got tired and quit.

　○ New machines were invented. News could travel faster with the new machines.

INFERENCE

6 **Why do you think Charlie was mentioned in this passage?**

　○ He liked to ride horses.

　○ He lived in 1860.

　○ Even though he was only eleven years old, he rode for the Pony Express.

PERSONAL RESPONSE

7 **Would you have wanted to ride for the Pony Express? Why or why not?**

I _____ have wanted to ride for the Pony Express
　　would　　　would not

because _____

_____

_____

✓ Check and Correct →

Reread your answers.
Do your answers make sense? ☐
Do you have a capital at the beginning of each sentence
　and a period at the end? ☐
Did you use your best handwriting? ☐

SCORING　　　　　　　　　　　　　　　Date _____

Topic ___ /1	Goal, Vocabulary ___ /1	Supporting Details ___ /4	Main Idea ___ /1
Drawing Conclusions ___ /1	Inference ___ /1	Personal Response ___ /1	Total ___ /10

Teachers: If you wish to keep a cumulative record of student assessment scores, see the *Assessment Manual*.

Name _____

Date _____

A Tall Tale: John Henry

Note

- Before beginning the assessment, have students read the title.
  Have students read the warm-up words in the box on the next page.
- Then have students complete the assessment on their own.

WARM-UP

glowed	whirlwind	challenged	steam drill	mountain

A Tall Tale: John Henry

John Henry worked on the railroad. He was the biggest, strongest, fastest man with a hammer there ever was. One day, a stranger came and showed the workers a new machine called a steam drill. He said the machine was faster and stronger than any man. John Henry challenged him to a contest.

Who could break up the rock and make a tunnel through the mountain first? John Henry and the steam drill both began to hammer at the rock. The machine puffed and shook. John Henry held a twenty-pound hammer in each hand. His strong arms whirled through the air. The ringing of his hammer was heard a hundred miles away. Sparks flew from the steel, and his hammers glowed white-hot. Men had to throw cool water on him to keep him from burning up. The steam drill broke down, but John Henry kept going like a whirlwind. When he broke through the other side of the mountain, the crowd cheered.

John Henry finally put down his hammers. For the first time in his life, he was tired. "I did my best," he said. "A man is nothing but a man."

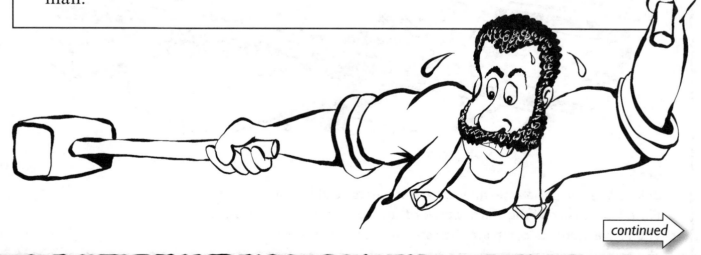

continued

CHARACTERIZATION, WEB

1 **Complete the web by writing words that describe John Henry.**

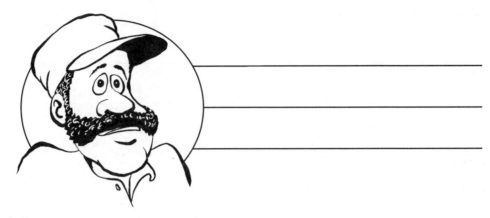

_____

_____

_____

CHARACTERIZATION, WRITTEN RESPONSE

2 **Describe John Henry. Write at least two sentences.**

_____

_____

_____

_____

_____

BEGINNING

3 **What happened at the _beginning_ of the story?**

○ John Henry challenged the man to a contest.

○ John Henry's arms whirled through the air, and his hammer glowed white-hot.

○ The steam drill puffed and shook.

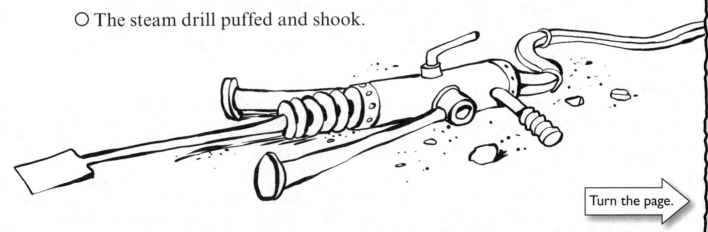

Turn the page.

DRAWING CONCLUSIONS

4 **Why do you think John Henry won the contest?**

John Henry won the contest because _____

_____

_____

GENRE

5 **This story is . . .**

      ○ fiction.   ○ nonfiction.

GENRE/VOCABULARY— TALL TALE

6 **Tall tales are imaginative stories with *exaggerations* and characters that are bigger than life. Which of these sentences makes the story about John Henry a tall tale?**

    a. John Henry worked on the railroad.

        Does this make the story of John Henry a tall tale?   yes   no

    b. John Henry was able to tunnel through the mountain with just two hammers.

        Does this make the story of John Henry a tall tale?   yes   no

    c. John Henry beat the steam drill in tunneling through the mountain.

        Does this make the story of John Henry a tall tale?   yes   no

    d. John Henry worked hard and always did his best.

        Does this make the story of John Henry a tall tale?   yes   no

SCORING   Date _____

Characterization ____ /1	Characterization ____ /2	Beginning ____ /1
Drawing Conclusions ____ /1	Genre ____ /1	Vocabulary ____ /4
		Total ____ /10

Teachers: If you wish to keep a cumulative record of student assessment scores, see the *Assessment Manual.*

Name _____

Date _____

Unit 17 Food Chains

Sun

Grass

Deer

Cougar

Note
- Before beginning the assessment, have students read the title.
  Have students read the warm-up words in the box on the next page.
- Then have students complete the assessment on their own.

Frogs in the Food Chain

Frogs are important animals in the food chain. They have lived on Earth since the time of the dinosaurs. Think about that! Frogs have been in the food chain for millions of years.

Why are frogs an important part of the food chain? All living things need energy. Many animals get energy from frogs. Energy passes from the sun to green plants. Green plants make their own food. Then herbivores eat the green plants, and carnivores eat the herbivores. Frogs are part of this food chain.

Here's how it works. Frogs eat insects, worms, and spiders. Then birds, snakes, and fish eat the frogs. Bats, foxes, and even some people enjoy a tasty frog meal. Think about that! Frogs give other animals the energy to live and grow.

Today, there are more than four thousand different kinds of frogs. They live in trees, lakes, and ponds. They live in swamps and wetlands. They live on almost every continent. Frogs are an important part of food chains all over the world.

continued

MAIN IDEA

1 **What is the main idea of "Frogs in the Food Chain"?**

○ Some people eat frogs.

○ Frogs eat insects, worms, and spiders.

○ Frogs are important in the food chain.

SUPPORTING DETAILS, CHART

2 **Write facts that support the main idea.**
If you need to, look in the passage.

Topic/Main Idea: Frogs are important in the food chain.

Fact 1	Fact 2	Fact 3	Fact 4
Frogs have been in the food chain for ___ ___ ___	They eat ___ ___ ___ ___ ___	___ ___ ___ ___ ___	Frogs are found in food chains ___ ___ ___

FACT SUMMARY, WRITTEN RESPONSE

3 **Using the facts you've listed, write a paragraph that explains how frogs are important in the food chain. Start with the main idea. Then write at least three supporting details. Use your own words.**

_____

_____

_____

_____

Turn the page.

Unit 17 Written Assessment
(continued)

✓ Check and Correct
Reread your paragraph.

Does your paragraph make sense? ☐
Do you have a capital at the beginning of each sentence and a period at the end? ☐
Did you use your best handwriting? ☐

VOCABULARY—ENERGY

4 **Food chains are all about *energy*. You are part of food chains. What do you need energy to do?**

I need energy to _____

_____

Bonus

Draw a food chain. It can be any food chain you wish.
You can look in your storybook for ideas.

plant   herbivore   carnivore

SCORING

Main Idea ___ /1	Supporting Details ___ /4	
Fact Summary ___ /4	Vocabulary ___ /1	Total _____ /10

Teachers: If you wish to keep a cumulative record of student assessment scores, see the *Assessment Manual*.

Name _____

Date _____

Sea Snakes

Note
- Before beginning the assessment, have students read the title.
  Have students read the warm-up words in the box on the next page.
- Then have students complete the assessment on their own.

WARM-UP

| carnivores | approximately | paddle | poisonous |

Sea Snakes

You might have read about snakes that live on land. But did you know that there are approximately 70 different kinds of snakes that live in the ocean?

Sea snakes look a lot like their land relatives, yet they are different. Most sea snakes have a tail that is shaped like a paddle, and their bodies are flatter than land snakes. These things help them to swim. Most sea snakes can't move on land at all.

Like all reptiles, sea snakes breathe air. They come to the surface to breathe. They can also get air from the water through their skins. Sea snakes can stay underwater for as long as two hours.

Sea snakes are carnivores. They hunt for fish by poking their heads into cracks and holes where fish are hiding. Their bite is poisonous. Luckily for us, they don't usually bite people!

continued →

TOPIC

1 **What is this passage about?**

This passage is about _____

FACTS/SUPPORTING DETAILS, CHART

2 **Write facts that support the main idea.**
If you need to, look back at the passage.

Main Idea: Sea snakes are interesting reptiles that live in the sea.

Fact 1	**Fact 2**	**Fact 3**
Sea snakes have a tail that is shaped	Sea snakes get air from the water through	

FACT SUMMARY, WRITTEN RESPONSE

3 **Using the facts you've listed, write a paragraph that tells why sea snakes are interesting reptiles. Start with the main idea. Then write at least three supporting details. Use your own words.**

_____

_____

_____

_____

_____

_____

Turn the page.

VOCABULARY—APPROXIMATELY

4 **The passage says that *approximately* 70 different kinds of snakes live in the ocean. What does that mean?**

○ There are exactly 70 snakes left in the ocean.

○ About 70 different kinds of snakes live in the ocean.

○ A sea snake can live for 70 years.

FACT

5 **The passage gives us other facts about sea snakes. Check the sentence that is a fact.**

__ A sea snake can stay underwater for two hours.

__ A sea snake can stay underwater for two days.

✓ Check
and Correct

Reread your answers.

Do your answers make sense? ☐

Do you have a capital at the beginning of each sentence
and a period at the end? ☐

Did you use your best handwriting? ☐

SCORING   Date _____

Topic ___/1	Supporting Details ___/3	Fact Summary ___/4
Vocabulary ___/1	Fact ___/1	Total ___/10

Teachers: If you wish to keep a cumulative record of student assessment scores, see the *Assessment Manual*.

Name _____

Date _____

Antone's Absurd Adventure

Note
- Before beginning the assessment, have students read the title.
  Have students read the warm-up words in the box on the next page.
- Then have students complete the assessment on their own.

WARM-UP

Antone	antennas	bacon	spotless

Antone's Absurd Adventure

Antone didn't like chores. Today he had to clean out the hot, dusty shed. Instead of sweeping, he took a break behind the shed where his mother couldn't see him. He noticed a trail of ants and lay down to watch.

Antone marveled at how hard the little ants worked. Just watching them made him tired.

Suddenly, Antone got smaller, and antennas sprouted from his head. Before he could panic, he was jostled by one of the ants. "No time to dawdle," said the ant.

"But I'm not an ant," Antone said in his most polite voice. "Ordinarily, I'm a boy."

"Perhaps you were a boy," the ant replied, "but now you're an ant. Back to work!"

Antone led the ants to the garbage can where he knew they would find leftovers from breakfast. As he lifted a big chunk of bacon, he was jostled again. "Back to work!" He recognized the voice. "Wake up," said his mother.

Antone sat up and counted his arms and legs—only two of each! He marched back into the shed and worked like an ant until it was spotless. Antone had learned a good lesson from his adventure as an ant.

continued

SEQUENCE OF EVENTS, CHART

1 **Fill in the chart to show the chain of events in the story.**

First Event

Antone took a break from cleaning the shed to watch

_____

_____

▼

Next Event

Suddenly, _____

_____

_____

▼

Next Event

Antone led the ants to the

garbage can so _____

_____

_____

▼

Conclusion

Antone heard his mother tell

him to _____

_____

_____

RETELL, WRITTEN

2 **Using your list of events, write about Antone's Absurd Adventure.**

First, _____

_____

_____

_____

Then, _____

_____

_____

_____

Next, _____

_____

_____

_____

Finally, _____

_____

_____

_____

_____

Turn the page.

VOCABULARY—ABSURD

3 **What made this story *absurd*?**

○ Antone didn't like chores.

○ Antone turned into an ant.

○ Antone counted his arms and legs.

LESSON

4 **What lesson did Antone learn from his dream?**

○ It's good to work hard like an ant.

○ Always be polite to ants.

○ The grass is always greener behind the shed.

✓ Check and Correct →

Reread your answers.

Do your answers make sense? ☐

Do you have a capital at the beginning of each sentence
and a period at the end? ☐

Did you use your best handwriting? ☐

SCORING   Date _____

Sequence of Events ___ /4	Retell ___ /4	
Vocabulary ___ /1	Lesson ___ /1	Total ___ /10

Teachers: If you wish to keep a cumulative record of student assessment scores, see the *Assessment Manual*.

Name _____

Date _____

The Amazing Brain

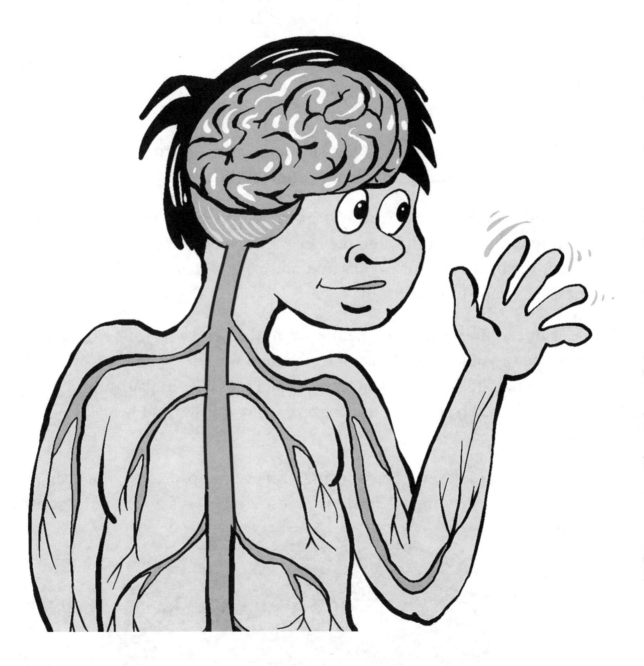

Note
- Before beginning the assessment, have students read the title.
  Have students read the warm-up words in the box on the next page.
- Then have students complete the assessment on their own.

WARM-UP

control	messages	communicates	siren

The Amazing Brain

Your brain looks like a blob of chewed bubble gum. It is pink and covered with cracks. Even though it doesn't look important, it is the control center of your body.

The brain controls thinking. It even controls your heartbeat and breathing. Your brain is in charge of everything you do.

Your brain communicates with every part of your body. It sends messages that travel through the nerves. The nerves carry the messages out of the brain to your organs and muscles. The nerves also send messages back to your brain.

For example, when you hear a siren, the nerves in your ears send a message to your brain. "Listen to the loud noise." When you see the fire engine, the nerves in your eyes send a message to your brain. "Hey, look at the red truck." You recognize what you see and hear. It's a fire engine!

Your brain never stops working. It never stops to rest, not even when you are sleeping. A brain isn't just a blob. It's an amazing control center!

continued

TOPIC

1 **What is this passage about?**

This passage is about _____

SUPPORTING DETAILS, CHART

2 **Topic: The Brain . . .**
Fill in the supporting details in the box.

- controls _____
  _____

- controls _____
  _____
  _____

- communicates _____
  _____
  _____

- never _____
  _____

MAIN IDEA, CHART

3 **What is the main idea?**
(Start with *The brain . . .*)

_____

_____

_____

_____

_____

○ stops working when you sleep.

○ is the control center of your body.

○ is a blob of chewing gum.

IDENTIFYING–FACT

4 **What carries messages back and forth from your brain to your organs and muscles?**

○ feet

○ hands

○ nerves

Turn the page.

VOCABULARY–CONTROL

5 **The brain *controls* everything in the body. What is another way to say that?**

○ The brain breaks down everything in the body.

○ The brain is in charge of everything in the body.

○ The brain obeys everything in the body.

DRAWING CONCLUSIONS, WRITTEN RESPONSE

6 **If you saw smoke coming out of a building, and you saw a fire engine pulling up to the building, what would your brain do? Write at least two sentences. (Start with *My brain would…*)**

_____

_____

_____

_____

_____

✓ Check and Correct ⟹

Reread your answers.

Do your answers make sense? ☐

Do you have a capital at the beginning of each sentence and a period at the end? ☐

Did you use your best handwriting? ☐

SCORING   Date _____

Topic ___ /1	Supporting Details ___ /4	Main Idea ___ /1
Identifying–Fact ___ /1	Vocabulary ___ /1	Drawing Conclusions ___ /2
		Total ___ /10

Teachers: If you wish to keep a cumulative record of student assessment scores, see the *Assessment Manual.*

Cushion Activity
Use anytime

Name _____

Unit _____ Story Title _____

My Favorite Story Part

Copy your favorite part of the story. Then draw a picture to illustrate it.

_____

_____

_____

_____

_____

_____

Name _____

Unit _____ Story Title _____

My Favorite Story Part

Copy your favorite part of the story. Then draw a picture to illustrate it.

_____
_____
_____
_____
_____